THE COMING OI

The Bloodking comes!

The old wall is a border: Englar
North, light and darkness.

It is 1745, and the long-awaited night as come. The Bloodking calls his army to battle, and armed with the powers of the undead and the damned, he will bring them South to claim his birthright: The throne of Britain.

Only the old Watchers on the wall stand in his way. They, their swords, and their faith. But too much time has passed and the Watch has grown slack and ill-prepared for the coming war. Only Martin and Sean have seen the horrors that lie ahead for humankind. Only they have the power to stop it.

Now, two young officers of the Watch have a duty to perform:

Stop the Bloodking.

Or die trying.

PRAISE FOR THE COMING OF THE KING

"...horrifying Highland vampires from the bloodline of the diabolical Stuarts. This first novel...offers excitement that never slackens." -- Margaret L. Carter, author of the Eppie Award-winning vampire novel DARK CHANGELING

"...superb story. Thoroughly enjoyable from the first word to the last. William Meikle has a wonderfully unique style..." -- The Eternal Night Science Fiction, Fantasy and Horror

"Breathtaking, Scary and Original. A must read. An impressive blend of horror, history and imagination." -- Dave Dreher, Horror News Network

"I was captivated from the very first scene...Very well written." -- Patricia Altner, author of Vampire Readings: An Annotated Bibliography

GRYPHONWOOD BOOKS
BY WILLIAM MEIKLE

The Watchers Trilogy
The Coming of the King
The Battle for the Throne
Culloden!

The Midnight Eye Files
The Amulet
The Sirens
The Skin Game

Berserker
The Invasion
The Valley
Island Life
Concordances of the Red Serpent

THE COMING OF THE KING

BOOK ONE OF THE WATCHERS TRILOGY

WILLIAM MEIKLE

Gryphonwood

ISBN-10: 1-940095-46-8
ISBN-13: 978-1-940095-46-2

CHAPTER 1

JANUARY, 1649 THE TOWER OF LONDON

They waited until just before dawn before they came for him. Even though the sky was becoming light, still they carried flaming torches they were careful to keep between themselves and the doorway to his cell.

He was dreaming but not asleep. He had not slept for a very long time, but the dreams came anyway, with more regularity as his confinement grew ever longer.

His cell was no more than a five-foot cube—too short for either standing upright or lying out straight. It was made even more confined by the thick iron chains they used to bind him. Many times since they put him here he had tested their strength, but they were secure and solid, like the old tower itself, and as he grew weaker there was less and less chance of him breaking free.

Stagnant water ran down the walls, and occasionally, when the river flooded, he found himself almost knee-deep in raw sewage. The straw at his feet had not been changed for over a month, and the smell as it rotted suffused his clothes, his hair, even—he began to suspect—his skin.

He had not fed for a long time, except for the occasional rat that wandered into the cell by mistake, and he didn't count that as feeding. He was aware that he had lost a lot of weight, and must look gaunt and haggard, but that suited his captor's purpose—they would want him looking pale and wasted for the show to come.

"It is today?" he asked, as the guards opened the cell door. They muttered prayers under their breath, and one made a stabbing motion with his fingers to ward off the evil eye before motioning that he come out.

"Ironhead has finally made up his mind," he said. It wasn't a question, and they didn't contradict him. One of them nodded, but didn't speak. They eyed him warily as he shuffled from the cell.

He could smell them from here, the stink of the bulb overpowering everything, even their sweat. Even now, when he had fallen as far as it was possible to fall, they still feared him.

And so they should. Once he had held not one but two countries in the palm of his hand and the whole of Europe trembled. Now he was reduced to this.

They washed him, none too gently, taking care to keep away from the reach of his teeth, and they didn't remove the chains. He hissed, and thrashed his head, but the heavy chains stopped him from getting close to them, and his heart wasn't really in it. All that was left was to die a good death and spit in the face of the Ironhead.

He asked for his best finery, and was surprised that he was allowed it. They put him back in the cell, unlocked the chains, and passed him the clothes he was to die in.

The feel of the dark silk against his skin was welcome after the years of coarse sackcloth, and having the weight of the chains taken away lifted his spirits. He thought once more of escape, but he knew that to try it would be futile at this late stage. He was too weak, and he had waited too long. When they told him it was time he held out his arms and allowed the chains to be locked in place for one last time.

"Do you wish a man of the cloth?" the largest of his guards asked. They were the first words that had been spoken to him since his so-called trial.

In return he merely laughed in their faces.

"Why, does he taste good?"

He saw the disgust in their faces. Once there had been love in faces like these—once he had commanded the respect of the country. He had miscalculated the timing of showing them his true face, and that was what had brought him to this pass—the country wasn't yet ready to be ruled by the likes of him. Even then he might have prevailed, given time, but Ironhead had thwarted him, both here in London, and again in Edinburgh. And when he was brought through the country in his chains the crowds that had once cheered came out in their thousands to mock, even though the journey by necessity took place after sunset.

With the silks on he felt more like his old self. He had been worried that he did not have the strength for what was to come, but now, in his finery, he would show the mundane masses how a real aristocrat dies.

After all, he had died once before, and it had only made him stronger. The bloodline was secure and safe, his claim to the throne had been legitimized, and one day his son would take this land for his own.

In the meantime, he would die like the king he was.

They took him out of his cell and down the short steps of the tower stairs. He did not fight them as they tied his hair back, only insisting that they used silk for the purpose. He stood tall as the guards checked his chains for one last time before leading him out to face the crowd.

It seemed as if all of London was here, a throng jostling and pushing as they forced their way in to the tower grounds. Hawkers in the crowd were selling corn dolls made in his image, and he saw several of them being burnt and stamped on. There were bakers selling their wares, and beggars scrambling around in the mud for scraps. Around the perimeter, on the old citadel walls, the Protector's personal guard stood watch, looking outwards. The prisoner wondered if his son would come, but one glance at the sky told him it was too late.

Children held tightly to the hands of their parents, and wives clung to husbands, and none would meet him in the eye.

He cursed them for their drabness, their grey and black clothing and their sterile religion. In turn they spat at him, and poked their fingers to ward off the evil eye. But all the time he simply smiled, showing his teeth.

The only bare spot in the crowd was out in the middle, a simple bench atop a plinth, the rough wood partially covered by a clean white cloth.

"A sacrifice at the altar—the end of all true kings," he said, shouting to make himself heard, and, smiling still, he showed the crowd his teeth again.

They parted for him, as if afraid to be too close. There was no shouting, no insults, merely silence, until someone started up a drumbeat, deep and sonorous, matching time with his paces.

"May you rot in hell," a voice shouted to his left, and he turned to find himself facing a young girl. She was quite pretty, in a peasant sort of way. So he put the charm in his eyes forcing his last strength into it, and she came to him, and, before his guards comprehended what was happening, he kissed her, just once, on the mouth, drawing a little blood and leaving a smear on the corner of her lip as the guards dragged her off. She looked back at him over her shoulder, her eyes glazed, the charm still working.

"Anyone else want the last gift of the King?" he shouted. "I can mend all your ills and you will never die, never grow old. Join me and I will make you a Lord."

But no one came forward. All who would have followed him had long since been weeded out by the Ironhead and the charm was used up—he was too weak.

Time was when he had entranced whole armies, and now he was trembling after using just one girl. He had truly fallen far.

As he approached the plinth he could see his old adversary waiting for him.

The drumbeat stopped and the crowd fell silent as his enemy began to speak.

"You have been tried and convicted of crimes against Parliament and humanity. Today, we the people judge you, and find you wanting."

The voice echoed around the tower grounds, and only the cawing of ravens broke the silence before the old man continued.

"Here, in the sight of God, I ask you to repent your deeds. He will surely not admit you to Paradise, but He may spare you the tortures of Hell."

The prisoner rattled his chains.

"Hell cannot be worse than this, old man. I repent

nothing. My god made me what I am, and I am king by right and by justice. I say to you that you are the one who should repent, for surely vengeance shall be mine."

The old man stepped up to him, and spoke in a low voice, so that the crowd could not hear.

"Your kind will never have the throne again—I will see to that."

The prisoner smiled again, and bared his teeth.

"Come closer brother. I would kiss you one last time."

The old man kept his distance, and motioned to the guards. The prisoner was led up to the table, and forced to lie on top of it, face upwards, his wrists and ankles manacled to its corners.

Clouds scudded overhead—the only thing he could see. The sky was beginning to lighten, and he felt a tingling on his skin, but there was plenty of time for what was to unfold. He wondered if he would be given leave to look at the sun for one last time.

The drum began pounding again, and the crowd cheered as a figure dressed all in black ascended the plinth. A hood covered his head, with only small slits for the eyes. The prisoner did not know him.

"Strike hard and firm," he said. "The sun is bad for my complexion."

The hooded man smiled, a thin thing that didn't reach his eyes, but he didn't speak.

"Do you have any last words?" the Ironhead said, and the prisoner smiled once more, before shouting, loud enough for all to hear.

"Forgive them father, for they know not what they do."

The hooded man's arm went up, and came down, and a wooden stake was pounded straight through the heart of the prisoner and down into the table, pinning him there. The crowd, as one, gave out a sigh, but there was no other noise as time seemed to stand still for a long moment.

Blood burst from the body, a raging torrent that sprayed the nearer crowd and bubbled and seethed in a pool under the bench. There was a scream, so loud that the ravens jumped into jerky flight and the watching crowd shivered, as if a sudden chill wind had passed through them.

The sun came up over the rim of the tower wall, and the body began to burn, slowly at first, then with a white flame that threatened to sear the eyes of the onlookers.

Within the fire something squirmed, and although the flame was so hot that the onlookers had to stand back, still it screamed and flailed. Those close to the inferno would later swear that, at the last, even as the screaming went on and on, the heat was such that the iron of the chains was beginning to melt and run.

And then it was over. There was one final flash of white heat, then there was only a vague shape on the bench where the body had been. Small flickers of orange flame ran over the surface, but it was the old wood that was burning now.

When the fire finally stopped the old man known as Ironhead took the ashes and scattered them to the wind.

"Let this be the last!" he shouted. "No more will England suffer itself to be ruled by an Other. We stand, united, as one. One nation under God."

Several of the larger ashes fell to the ground and the crowd dispersed, leaving the ravens to pick among the small bones that were all that was left of Charles Stuart, King of England and Scotland.

CHAPTER 2

26th OCTOBER, 1745 HADRIAN'S WALL

The watch bell tolled twice as Martin went through the postern gate, and it was a full minute later before he heard the rushed footsteps behind him as Sean caught him up.

"The Thane will be having your guts for gaiters if he finds out." Martin said, having to shout to make himself heard above the rushing of the wind as they left the relative shelter of Milecastle and headed out onto the wall. "I hope she was worth it."

"Every minute and some more besides," the younger man said with a smile and a lascivious rub of his groin. "I'm surprised that I'm even able to walk."

Martin often wondered how Sean managed it. At nearly twenty Martin was two years older, but so far his only conquests had been on the training fields for battle. Whereas Sean already seemed to have worked his way through all the available women in the village—and some of the not so available ones.

"Besides," Sean continued, "The old man will be tucked up in his bed with the Good Book by now—it is only lost sinners like you and I who would be out and about on such a night. And I have no intention of telling anyone else how the Fisherman's wife spends her nights. Not even your father."

Sean waved a hand expansively and, as if on cue, the wind raised itself up a notch and the rain splattered more heavily against their faces.

"You wouldn't go telling the old man on me. Would you?" Sean said, and the ever-present smile was on his face. "After all, telling tales is a sin."

"My only sin was to stop you getting yourself killed by Edward Shoreman" Martin replied. "If I hadn't come into that byre when I did he would have found you and his wife instead of me."

"Aye, there's truth in that I suppose," said Sean. "But at least I didn't try to burn down the barn to hide the evidence."

Martin's ears burned. It was two weeks ago now. He'd only gone into the barn to check on a pregnant heifer. The surprise he'd got when he found Sean and the fisherman's wife together had made him drop the torch he was carrying, and the resultant flames had almost reached the barn roof before he and Sean managed to subdue them. They'd been found by the watch, smoke blackened and charred, standing in the ruins of the fire and laughing at the top of their voices.

It was probably the laughing that had caused the Thane to award them penal watch duty—the Keeper of Milecastle was not keen on any personal enjoyment getting in the way of duty.

"Seems you got all of the shame and none of the pleasure. But never mind," said Sean, wrinkling his nose to emphasise the point. "She smells of herring anyway."

That brought laughter from them both before they took another long look round, assessing the weather.

"Are we heading out onto the tops, or shall we just wait here and say later that all is quiet?" Sean said. "No one else will be out on a night like this—we may as well take it easy."

But after the escapade in the barn Martin was loath to risk the Thane's wrath again. Besides, although Sean believed them less than worthwhile, Martin took his watch duties seriously.

"You wait here if you want to," he said to the younger man. "I'll just have a quick tour and check in with the next watch up the line."

Sean laughed again.

"You can't think I'd let you out there on your own do you—there might be some farmer's daughter needing rescuing. Come on then. What are we waiting for?"

The first hundred yards were uphill into the wind and a small river of muddy water ran down the well-trodden path. They had to be careful to avoid soaking their boots—they both knew from long experience how long it would take to dry out afterwards. They walked on in silence, climbing higher along the ridge above Milecastle, both of them needing all their breath to force a passage against the elements.

The wind had been howling for three days now, a storm from the east that whistled across the high tops and dumped sudden squalls of sleeting rain in the valleys. The sheep had all been brought in off the hills and the only living things abroad in the night were the watch guards and the occasional rook caw-cawing overhead as it struggled to make headway.

The path got much steeper here, the ground beneath their feet slippery with mud and wet grass. The rain reached a new level of intensity, small biting flurries battering against the young men's cheeks and plastering their already wet clothing against their damp bodies. The blackness was complete, and only the fact that they knew this path well kept them from straying.

Martin looked out over the wall and wondered, as he did every day, if the watch was fulfilling any useful purpose and realising, again as he did every day, that it didn't matter if nothing ever came out of the North. The only thing that mattered was that the people of his small community knew that the watchers were keeping them safe. He turned and looked back down the valley to his home.

The fort of Milecastle butted up hard against the old Roman fortifications. It had originally been no more than a square keep. But after the battles against the Bruce it had been rebuilt in the Norman manner and, over the years, had grown extensions and enhancements and turrets until it now sprawled over twenty acres or more. Only the north-facing wall survived unscathed and unchanged.

To the south of the castle there was a wide area of open farmland, pastures and crop fields laboriously dug and maintained from the continually wet soil by generations of farmers. They bred them hardy enough around here, and with the requisite lack of imagination to survive in the constant shadow of menace.

But all that was only to be seen in the daylight. Now there was only more darkness. Barely visible, tiny lights flickered in some of the high windows of the castle and Martin knew that Sean had been wrong about the old man being abed. The

Thane would be sitting in one of those windows, his gaze always fixed to the North, waiting for an enemy who had never come.

Suddenly Sean pulled Martin into the lee of the wall.

"Let's wait this out—it can't get much worse."

Martin wasn't so sure, but was grateful for the rest even though the wall did little to shield them from the cutting wind.

"And at least we got a first." Sean said as he checked along the top of the wall to ensure that the chain of bulbs was secure. "You're the first son of a Thane ever to get penal guard duty at night."

Martin groaned.

"There is no need to remind me. It is something my father is never going to let me forget."

And as he said it he knew it was true. It was going to be many months before the Thane trusted him again, either as a leader or as his father. Martin had disappointed him on both counts.

The memory of the tongue-lashing he had received was too fresh, too raw. It was time to get Sean off the subject.

"But the guard is not the hardship it once was. They have not breached the wall for nigh on a hundred years. Not since the Old Protector sent them back to their mountains and executed the Blood King. I have heard that there are few left, even in the high places, and that people have gone ashore from the Islands and are rebuilding the towns."

"Aye. That story has been around the castle walls a few times," Sean said. "But I put as much faith in that as I do in the one about the Boy King from France coming back to reclaim the bloodline. Watch the walls, keep the bulbs fresh, and the other side can rot and fester till they have to feast on themselves—that's what I say."

"At least you and the Thane agree on something then." Martin said, getting a grunt in reply from Sean.

This was leading to an old conversation between them. Sean wanted to be doing something else, somewhere else, anywhere that wasn't this small community ringed by wall, fort and duty. Once he'd got as far as Carlisle before the officers of the watch had found him and whipped him into submission, for a couple of months anyway.

Martin's life was bound up in his duty, to his father, to the watch and to the town that he knew would one day be under his Thaneship. That's the way it had been for over four hundred years, the mantle passing from father to son, the reason lost somewhere in time.

Many times, as boys and men, they had stood on this wall together, Sean wondering what was out there in the wilderness beyond, Martin worrying that someday they might find out.

Sean saw Martin look out over the wall.

"I doubt if they're coming tonight. Let's just get the round done. This wind is likely to shrivel my manhood so much that the fisherwife is likely to mistake me for her husband."

Sean laughed, but Martin could only manage a smile. Something was abroad in the night, he could feel it, and it laid a damper on his spirits.

They moved away from the wall and back to the path. Martin noticed with some dismay that the wall was beginning to crumble in places. He knew for certain that his father would have to be told, just as he also knew for certain that he would be back out here with a work team in the morning.

Ten minutes later they reached the top of the ridge. Up here the wind howled even harder and the rain battered heavily against their heads. Martin noticed with dismay that the watch they were supposed to meet, here halfway between their stations, was nowhere to be seen.

"At least someone has more sense than ourselves," Sean said. But Martin knew it was just another thing to add to the list to report to the Thane. And if he knew his father, then these missing watchmen would regret missing their duty— they would be lucky to escape with only a flogging.

They waited on the top for ten minutes, but it was obvious that there would be no one to make the allotted appointment. After checking that the bulbs were still in place they turned back, happy to finally have the wind behind them.

"The Thane is truly sorely vexed with you?" Sean asked,

and this time it was Martin's turn to grunt in reply.

"Aye," he said. "But I believe that it's more disappointment than anger. It will pass. But I will be out here on many nights like this before it does."

"Then I will be here with you. After all, it was my pleasure that brought your pain. We will take our punishment together."

He punched Martin on the shoulder.

"Brothers?" he asked.

"Always," Martin replied, and returned the punch.

Together they headed back towards home, hearth and warmth. Martin could just make out the watch light on the postern gate about a hundred yards ahead of them when Sean pulled at his arm and pointed out over the wall and into the darkness beyond.

"Look." There was a tremor in his voice, a tone that Martin had never heard there before, a tremor that spoke of fear. "There's someone on the road."

At first Martin could see nothing but more rain and more blackness. It was impossible. Nothing had moved on that road in his lifetime, and for someone, or something, to be doing so now, in darkness, was almost inconceivable. He suspected a prank, remembering their conversation less than a quarter hour before.

Then he saw the light, a faintest glimmer of spluttering red and orange that bobbed and weaved as it followed the path of the old road that led to the long-closed watch gate of Milecastle.

Martin saw that it would be only a matter of minutes before whoever was out there reached the gate. He broke into a run and heard Sean following behind him.

David Brown was on guard at the gate, a youngster of barely fifteen summers.

"You saw it?" David asked. "Should we call out the watch?"

That had been Martin's first reaction, but it looked like there was only one light and, after the debacle in the byre, he was loath to incur the Thane's displeasure again so soon.

"Let's leave it until we know more," Martin replied. "We won't have to wait long. You stay out of sight," he said to the young man. "And at the first sign of trouble, then you can ring the bell as much as you want."

The lad didn't look too displeased at the prospect, and when Martin and Sean turned towards the gate he was already holding tight on the bell rope, his eyes wide and staring.

For the first time that night Martin felt the lack of his old musket and missed the heavy weight of his sword—two more casualties of the episode in the barn.

"Well, what do we do now?" Sean asked and Martin saw that the fear had left him as quick as it had come. Now there was only nervous anticipation.

He didn't have time to answer as a voice came from behind the gate.

"Sanctuary! Sanctuary! A Christian man and his family request sanctuary!"

Whatever Martin had expected from beyond the wall it certainly hadn't been a Christian. He climbed the stairs beside the heavy oak gate and looked down onto the road below.

The voice's owner was a heavy-built, heavily bearded man of about fifty. He was standing beside a small, stocky horse on which there was another, smaller, person whose features were completely wrapped up against the weather.

The bearded man raised a small brass oil lamp above his head and looked up at the figures on the wall.

"Sanctuary!" the voice cried again. "In the name of Jesus Christ, sanctuary!"

"He's one of us," Sean whispered. "The Others would never be able to use the name of our Lord."

Martin wanted to agree, but he had to be sure—the Thane would expect no less.

"The watch has orders not to allow anyone to pass by night," he shouted. "Come back in the morning and we will welcome you gladly. It is many years since we had news from beyond the wall."

The heavy-set man moved away from the pony and approached the wall until he was standing beneath Martin. He was dressed in the Highland style that Martin had heard of, but never seen—a heavy plaid over the top of a knee length kilt, their colours indistinguishable in the gloom. He was older than he had first appeared, and a recent scar ran in a livid line from just below his left eye to the point of his jaw. Now that Martin could see him more clearly, the extra gray in his hair and at his temples was more noticeable, but his eyes were blue and fierce and when he opened his mouth his teeth, although somewhat decayed, looked normal.

"If it's news you are wanting, I have plenty of that, and your elders are going to want to know about it tonight, not tomorrow. But have pity—my daughter is sick and needs heat and warmth if she is to survive this night."

Martin was beginning to waver, but Sean's next action settled the issue. The younger man lifted a bulb from the wall in front of him and tossed it to the man below.

The man caught it in one hand and, when he saw what it was, let out a laugh.

"What is this—an Englishman's idea of hospitality? Do you want me to plant it or rub it over my body?"

"Neither," Sean said. "You must eat it. It is the first test."

"A test now is it? Ah well, I've been tested before and have yet to be found wanting." He peeled the rough skin from the bulb and raised it to his mouth.

"Do I really need to eat this to prove what I am?"

Martin nodded and the bearded man shrugged, popped the clove into his mouth, chewed and swallowed. He grimaced and Sean suddenly had a dagger in his hand ready to throw.

The Scotsman rubbed his eyes with the back of his hand, then laughed with little humour.

"By God you grow an astringent herb in these parts—I've never tasted stronger—it'll be coming out in my sweat for weeks."

He threw back his head and laughed again, heartily this time.

"Here I am expecting a musket ball for my troubles, and I get two lads feeding me garlic."

He looked up at Martin.

"And now that I've passed your wee test do you think you might open the gate? Or do I have to report to my countrymen that English hospitality is all that they suspect it to be?"

Martin and Sean looked at each other. Sean nodded, and after a second, Martin did the same before turning back to the Scotsman.

"I will let you enter," said Martin. "But you will be taken before the Thane—he will decide what must be done. But I tell you this, sir: you will find that English hospitality is well served in the house of the Thane of Milecastle."

"Fine words lad, but it's time for actions. Do you open that muckle gate, or do I stand here until the rain rots it away?"

Martin sent young David ahead to rouse the Thane's household before he went to help Sean pull open the twin doors of the gate. Long unused hinges squealed in protest, and it took a great push from the man on the other side before they finally swung ajar.

The bearded man led the pony through, then helped Martin and Sean swing the doors close and drop the bolts.

When the job was completed he held out a hand that engulfed Martin's when he took it.

"Duncan Campbell at your service, young sirs. My sword is yours when you need an ally, my house is yours when you need a bed, and let no man call me a liar."

He also shook hands with Sean, and Martin was amused to notice that his friend came off worst when he tried to match grips. Duncan Campbell might look like an old man, but he had a strength that matched and then beat the best that Milecastle had to offer.

"We have thought for all these years that there were only the Others beyond the wall," Sean said.

The man's face was serious as he replied.

"Aye. For many years that's almost all there was. Some of us managed—and still do. But for how much longer, I wonder?"

He shook his head as if to clear it.

"But that's a story for your Thane and the elders of this fine place. Meanwhile, would you be having a physician? My daughter is in sore need of help."

Predictably Sean was first to respond at any mention of a female, but he had only gotten as far as moving towards the pony when the militia arrived in the small courtyard in front of the gate—all twenty of them armed to the teeth and spoiling for a fight. It looked like young Brown had done more than just raised the household—it looked like he had declared a full scale invasion.

Martin caught Duncan Campbell's arm as it was heading for his sword.

"No, man. You are under my protection. Sanctuary is what you asked for, and I'll make sure you get it. Did you hear that," he said, raising his voice. "This man is under my personal protection."

"We must stake him," a voice said, but it didn't sound like there was the will for the task.

"There'll be no staking. This man asked for sanctuary in the Lord's name, and he passed the test of the bulb. Any harm comes to him from any of you and they'll have to answer to me."

He thought he heard a snort of derision from Sean but he had the attention of the rest of them. He dispatched young Brown to fetch the physician and led his new found responsibilities towards the main hall where he knew he'd have to answer to his father.

"Let me talk to the Thane first," he said to Duncan in a low voice that wouldn't carry to the rest. "He is not a man to take in travellers readily—even those from this side of the wall."

He was vaguely aware that Sean was sticking very close to the wrapped figure on the pony, and wondered if he should have insisted on talking to her before opening the gate. But it was too late for recriminations—his father would be waiting on the high seat.

They had just passed into the central quadrangle when young Brown returned at a run.

"The physician says he does not make calls on travellers at this time of the night, but if they would go to him, he will see them in his rooms," he said, one hand clasped tight to his dagger the whole time.

"Sean?" Martin said in a low voice. "Will you take charge of the girl?"

He saw the eager look in the younger man's eye.

"I'm trusting you with this," Martin said. "Maybe we have made a mistake here, but I don't think so. The Thane however might see things differently."

Sean looked Duncan Campbell in the eye.

"I request your leave to accompany your daughter to the physician," he said. "I pledge to you that I shall keep all harm from her."

"It's too late for that." Campbell muttered, but he took the outstretched hand that Sean offered.

"Look after her. I will look for you after we have seen your Elders, but if they will listen to my story it could be a long night. A long night for all of us."

Martin watched Sean lead the pony and its burden across the inner quadrangle. Suddenly he felt alone, a small boy again until a warm hand was placed on his shoulder.

"Come, young sir." Campbell said. "And let us impress on your elders the urgency that my mission here demands."

The officers of the watch crowded around them, jostling and shoving, and Martin had to pull rank as an officer before they let both him and the Scotsman through.

They were stopped at the door to the large hall, which was closed for the first time in Martin's memory.

Young John Barnstable stood in front of it, a sword held in front of him.

"Halt, in the name of the Thane," he said, and there was a distinct tremble in his voice.

"Let me pass, Johny," Martin said. But the younger man raised his sword higher.

"Tonight it is Officer Barnstable, sir," he said. "The Protector demands to know who asks for entry." The sword trembled slightly, but the voice was stronger now.

"The Protector is not here," Martin said, feeling the first flare of anger rise inside him. "I bring a Christian seeking sanctuary."

"That remains to be seen" the officer said.

"Aye, maybe," Martin said. "But it is for the Thane to decide, not you. Or your father."

He saw immediately that he had hit a nerve. The boy flinched, and did not protest when Martin stepped past him and pushed open the oak door.

The first thing that Martin noticed in the Great Hall was the heat. The fire in the huge hearth had recently been kindled with new wood added to the embers which had been lying there from the night before. The hall was filling up fast as the news of an arrival spread, and the mood was not good. Martin could see the distrust on faces that he was more used to seeing laughing, and there was enough weaponry on display to do battle with a small army.

The Thane's features mirrored those of his people, but he didn't speak as Martin approached him. The old man sat in the high chair, a rough-cut granite block that was rumoured to be as old as the original fortifications on which the Thaneship was built. A local legend told that Hadrian himself had supervised the building of the wall from this very chair, but at this moment Martin thought that no Emperor could have looked more imposing or sterner than the old Thane.

"Father," he began, but was stopped by a raised hand before he could continue.

"Your father is not here. Not this night. It is the Thane who will hear you." The voice was gruff and there was no trace of affection in the old man's eyes as he continued, raising his voice to ensure that the assembly could hear.

"Bring forth your traveller and let us judge his worth."

Campbell stepped forward. There was a murmur in the crowd, and a rattling of swords, but the Scotsman stood straight and tall and stared back at them. He cut an outlandish figure in this place of gray and black. The deep vibrant blue of his kilt and plaid seemed to shine in the candlelight, and his hair, long and curly in the manner of old, seemed to mock the severity of cut in evidence among the rest of the room. He still carried his sword, a long, ridiculously heavy thing. But Martin well remembered the stories of how the fighting Scots could remove a man's head with one cut, and didn't think anyone in the room would be willing to find out if they were true.

"I am Duncan Campbell, Clan Chief of the Campbells of Glenfinan, and I am in debt to your son for the giving of sanctuary."

His voice echoed around the room. Martin caught several glances being thrown his way, few of them friendly.

The Thane sighed deeply.

"We shall see which debts our watchman is responsible for presently," the old man said. "But first you must prove yourself before God."

"I tested him with the bulb," Martin began. "And he—"

Again he was silenced.

"Speak no more, watchman. You have done enough for one night," said a voice from behind him. He didn't have to turn to recognise the speaker. William Barnstable walked forward to take his place at the Thane's side—Chief Constable, owner of the byre so recently damaged, and the father of the boy who had barred their way to the hall.

The Constable had taken time to change into his uniform, the stark blackness of it in sharp contrast to Campbell's gaudy colours. His jaw was cleanly shaved, his tonsure neatly trimmed, and the black leather of his boots was polished to a sheen. He well knew the impression he was giving—to the assembled throng he made Campbell look like a barbarian. When he spoke his voice rang with the practice of a seasoned orator.

"You have allowed a stranger to enter from beyond the wall. For that you will answer to the council."

Martin was about to speak again when a warning look from the Thane stopped him.

"Bring out the Bible, and let the Lord be judge," the Thane said.

They stood in silence as they waited for the book to be

fetched, dark shadows flickering around them as the candles and the fire hissed and spluttered in the draughty hall.

The Bible was carried into the hall by John Barnstable, and although he had the strength built by many years of farm work, he struggled to keep hold of the massive book.

"This is the book of our fathers," the Thane said. "A record of our Thaneship and our succour in dark times. Come," he said to Duncan Campbell. "Come and lay your hand on it and show to me that my watchman has not been proved false."

Martin was about to step forward in protest, but was stopped by Duncan's hand on his arm.

"No, son. Your father is right. This is necessary, and I would do the same if I were sitting in his place."

He stepped towards the Thane, and a quiet fell over the room. Somewhere someone cocked a pistol, and there was the loud whisper of a sword being drawn from a scabbard.

Duncan Campbell looked the Thane in the eye.

"In the name of the Holy Trinity I swear that I am a man and a man only, and that while I draw breath I will be in debt to your watchman, your son, who showed Christian charity in a dark place where few other men would have given it."

And saying that he placed his right hand on the Bible.

"In the name of the Father, the Son, and the Holy Ghost," he said, and the Thane echoed the words before stretching out a hand in welcome.

"Well met, Campbell of Glenfinan."

William Barnstable stepped between them before they could clasp hands.

"That is not enough," he said. "We know nothing of this barbarian."

The Thane pushed the big man aside.

"We know he is a Christian. And if you cannot smell the bulb on his breath then it is time we had a new Constable. Shame on you, William."

He raised his voice that the whole hall might hear.

"He has passed the tests of the bulb and the Book and has proved himself a man, and only a man. We will welcome him as friend and brother."

Another murmur went through the hall, louder this time, and the elder Barnstable shouted above it.

"No. It is a trick. No one has come from the other side for a hundred years. We cannot trust anyone who does so now."

A roar of assent greeted him, and, not for the first time that night, Martin wished that he had not forfeited his weapons.

"And what would you have me do?" the Thane said, the sound of his voice instantly quieting the crowd. "Run him through the heart and see if he dies? You know as well as I do that only a man would pass the tests."

"Aye," said Campbell. "And I am a man who knew this test would come, but withstood it anyway, for I am a bearer of grave news that you need to hear, so let us talk and have no more of this nonsense."

"He mocks the tests," someone shouted.

"Barnstable is right," another voice proclaimed. "It's a trick. Kill him. Kill him now and be done with it."

Martin moved to stand beside Campbell.

"Anyone who wishes to harm this man will have to fight me first," he said, and was relieved to hear there was no tremor in his voice despite the sudden chill that seemed to flow in his veins. "I have given him Sanctuary. Would you have me made a liar and an oath-breaker?"

He looked at his father and was surprised to see a smile on the man's face.

"Duncan Campbell—you seem to have convinced my young watchman here, and as for myself, I am content with the results of the test and your fine speech. But have you anything else that might convince my Constable here?"

Duncan answered with a smile of his own.

"I'm afraid that the Constable will take more convincing than I am able to provide. But there is one more thing which the other fine people here might accept."

He drew aside his plaid, and there, hanging down on his chest and plain to see by all, was a large, heavy, silver cross.

He raised it to his lips and kissed it.

"This was given to me in Glenfinan by my brother, a Minister of the church, as he died two months ago. Two months ago when the Boy King from France raised the Standard of the Stewarts in Glenfinan and a hundred of my kinsmen died trying to stop him. Now will you hear my story?"

Suddenly the room was in uproar, with voices raised, in anger and then in fear. Several people left the room in a hurry, and Martin thought that would be the last he, or anyone else in Milecastle, would see of them. Barnstable was calling for quiet, but his voice was only one of many.

"Clear the hall, Constable," the Thane said. "Then join me in my rooms as soon as you can— there's a story here that needs to be told in private. Oh, and you'd better get some horses prepared—I've got a feeling that there are messages to be sent. And get the whole watch out onto the wall."

The Thane got up out of his chair, slowly, as if a great weight had suddenly descended on his shoulders. Martin moved forward but was brushed away as the old man stood up straight.

"So. The day has finally come. I've waited a long time. Too long, and now I feel old. Are we ready?"

Martin realised that his father was talking to him.

"As ready as we ever were, my Thane. You have kept the watch well."

"Aye," Duncan Campbell said. "Ready and waiting, and finally he has come. Will you hear my story now, Sir?"

The Thane nodded.

"Bring your friend to my room in the high tower," he said to Martin. "He has a tale to tell and I'm afeared that our lives depend on us listening."

Martin and Campbell followed the old man out of the hall. The crowd was already beginning to disperse, and the Constable was clearing up the last knots of dissenters with promises to let them know what was happening as soon as he did himself.

The turret stairs were sharp and winding, but the Thane

didn't seem to notice, bounding up them like a goat.

"He's not as old as he likes to appear," Campbell said. "That is good. You will need a strong leader."

"It is true then?" Martin asked. "The Boy King intends to bring back the old bloodline?"

"Aye. That and more besides," Campbell said. "But you will hear the whole story anon. I don't have the strength to tell it twice, so no more questions for now."

They followed the Thane up the stairs, through a thick oak door and into his chambers. A fire was already lit in the hearth and Martin helped his father drag four chairs around it, the last of which had to be brought away from the high, north-facing window. The Thane motioned that they should sit while he went into the adjoining ante-room to return with a pitcher of ale and four flagons.

"I've a feeling that your story will not be a short one," he said to Campbell. "And listening is also a thirsty business."

Campbell took a proffered flagon, raised it to his lips and drained half of it in one swallow, having to brush the foamy remnants from his heavy moustache.

"Long life and good health to all here," he said, motioning with his arm and including Barnstable who walked in at that moment.

The Constable ignored the Scotsman and stood beside the Thane.

"The horses are being readied, Sir, and the hall has been cleared, for now at least. But the people need to know what is happening."

"As do we all, William. Let us listen to what our guest has to say. We can make no decisions until we have his story."

Barnstable snorted at the word "guest", but took a flagon of ale and sat down, his eyes staring deep into the fire, never once looking at Martin or Campbell as the Scotsman began his story.

"I was born and raised in Arisaig on the West coast, about thirty miles to the west of the old fort on Loch Linne. I gather from your surprise at seeing me that no one beyond the wall even knew of the existence of men to the north. But we have been on the mainland since the Old Protector drove the Others into the high hills, and in pockets there are those who have never left, surviving even the rapacious days after Bannockburn.

"Oh, we still had to be careful, and we still lost people from time to time, but not like in the old days. The power of the Others was greatly diminished, and no more than a few hundred of them survived the Protector's purge. The sea was bountiful, the land was fertile, and good trade was to be had with the clans on the islands. All in all it was a good life.

"As you can see, I grew up strong, as did my brother Angus. I was the eldest, and would inherit the role of clan chief in time. My brother, whose cross you have seen, took holy orders across the sea in Ireland, and it was due to him that a church was built in Glenfinan. Our clan moved there twenty years since, when my father died and I became chieftain. And we prospered, although the Others did not like the presence of a house of God so close to land they considered their own. Three times they came, and each time, by the grace of God and the strength of good men, we sent them back to the hills. And eventually a truce of some kind prevailed."

The Constable snorted again.

"Fairy tales for children. I don't believe a word of it."

Campbell smiled back at him, but there was a cold gleam in his eye.

"Hear me out," he said. "And if you still insist on calling me a liar we can settle it in the courtyard in the morning."

He stared at Barnstable, his deep blue eyes seeming to blaze, and it was the Constable who broke off first, returning to gazing into the fire.

"It all changed on the night of 25th July, just over three months ago.

"I was in Arisaig visiting my daughter who was recently wed. Just after dusk a black shadow drew up in Loch nan

Uamh, and from it came a dreadful keening, the likes of which I hope never to hear again. It was as if a great cat was suffering all the torments of hell, a sound of pain and suffering that struck dread into all who heard it. And in answer to the keening, the dark shadows of the Others flowed down from the hills—the Macdonalds of Glencoe and the Camerons under Lochiel, Clanranald of Boisdale and more, from shadows older than memory. And out there on the loch they met, on a boat as black as sin. Du Teillay they called it, but to my clan it will for evermore be known as the Doom of the Campbells."

Duncan fell quiet and stared deep into the flame before emptying his flagon.

"And was it him? Was it the Boy King?" Martin asked.

When Campbell looked at him, Martin was surprised to see tears in the older man's eyes. "Aye. It was him all right, although I didn't know it then. Him and ten other black shadows as full of sin and pride as himself. And by morning the boat had gone, but I knew that an army had just been called to arms.

"Many of the people in Arisaig had fled during that night—several of the boats had gone from the harbour by morning. Of those that were left, some were mightily afraid. I managed to persuade some to come back with me to Glenfinan, but my daughter and her new husband were not to be moved. They, and some forty others, stayed behind as I led the remainder back to the sanctuary of the church.

"And for the next two weeks all was quiet. Some of the folk drifted back to Arisaig, but most stayed, and my brother's flock gained many new members."

He stopped again.

"May I trouble you for more of your fine ale? We are coming to the hard part of the tale, and my throat will need a good wetting before it can be told."

The pitcher was empty and Martin was sent to the ante-room for more. His mind was buzzing, full with images of black boats on dark lochs and shadows flitting through trees. What did it mean for his existence here? He didn't know, but he suspected that his life was about to change irrevocably, and not for the better either. He allowed himself an extra swallow of ale before returning to the group around the fireplace.

Barnstable was quiet now, and Martin could see that the Scotsman's story was beginning to affect him. The Thane seemed deep in thought, his head bowed and his hands clasped tightly in front of him. The Scotsman handed out his flagon to be refilled and took a long swallow before continuing.

"It was the night of 10th August. It had been a glorious day, with the sun beating down hard and only a light wind on the loch. I caught five big trout from the shore, and Angus and I broke bread together as we cooked them."

The Scotsman stopped, lost in thought.

"That was almost the last time we had together. Angus commented on how quiet it was, and how much he loved the place, and we wondered whether we had imagined the appearance of the boat off Arisaig. But just after nightfall we found out what the Boy King had been up to in the time since.

"They came with the sunset, my daughter and her man. He was sore wounded, bitten deep in the thigh, and the journey had done him in, but before he passed over he told of the army—yes, that's the word he used, the army of Others that had descended the night before on Arisaig. And the village had died in their beds, died and been recruited to swell the ranks. My daughter's man had managed to get them away, but they were the only two to escape.

"He passed over after telling his story, and we dispatched him in the old way, and Angus said the words over his remains. May God rest him, and may he stay sleeping in the ground.

"As for my daughter, she has been struck dumb, and no word has come from her from that night to this."

Martin put his hand on Campbell's shoulder.

"Our physician is a good man. He will bring her back to you."

Campbell went on talking as if he hadn't heard, his eyes

focused on somewhere far away, but not long enough ago.

"We barely had time to say the words over my newly lost kinsman when they fell on us in the darkness. Angus, Mary—my daughter—and I were near to the church and fell back there away from the screeching shadows that seemed to fill the night. When the screams began I was all for rushing out into the darkness, but I was stopped by Angus. He held me forcibly while outside the church my kinsmen were slaughtered and emptied, some of them taken as food, others, the strong ones, recruited to the cause. I ranted and raved, and even swore, there in the house of God, but still he held me.

"'I will not allow you to kill yourself,'" he said. "'And I would not see you lose your soul. You have the girl to think of. She is the last of our family. Promise me that you will put her first.'

"My clansmen were dying all around the village, their screams slowly fading to whimpers, and finally a deep silence. I went limp in his arms, and he relaxed his grip, just long enough to allow me to squirm away. I was out of the door before he could make a move to stop me.

"The Others were everywhere, flickering shadows in the darkness. The compound wall had been breached in three places at least, and there were men, real men, dragging the bodies of my clansmen away from the bulbs so that the Others could get to them. The sight of these men, once proud highlanders who had debased themselves to serve the Others, brought my blood to boiling point, and I charged out into the darkness with my sword flashing.

"I didn't get far. My charge was halted as if I had hit a wall, and I felt my sword being ripped from my hand. I was looking up into a pair of red eyes that seemed to see into my very soul, and I was about to give myself over to those eyes when Angus's voice brought me back to myself."

"'Begone demons! Go back to your master!'

"I was dropped unceremoniously on the ground and was lucky to be able to put my hand on my sword, but when I hefted it and turned to face my enemies, I found they were backing away from me. No, not from me, from something behind me. I turned to see Angus advancing from the church, his silver cross held out before him.

"'Get back to the church Duncan!' he shouted. 'There's nothing more you can do here. This is my work.'

"I moved behind him, but no further, as he advanced and the dark Others fell away in front of him. It seemed to me that the cross was shining with its own light, but it might have been no more than the reflection of the moon.

"Ten paces. That's as far as he got. Then the Others parted, and darker shadows emerged from their ranks. There were eleven of them, tall and silent, and they came forward, as if the cross meant nothing to them."

"'Go back!' Angus shouted, and I could hear the desperation in his voice. But still they came on until they had us trapped in the centre of a circle—a circle in which all I could see was blackness and eleven pairs of unblinking red eyes.

"Then one of the shadows came forward and seemed to become more solid, more real. It had been a young man, with long hair powdered white, and what looked like mummer's paint whitening his face and reddening his lips. He looked at my brother, then at the cross, and he smiled—a thing of menace that I hope never to see again.

"'Put it away brother,' he said. 'I have long since lost my fear of it—after all, what does one dead king have to fear from another?'

"And that was when I knew him for what he was. After all the stories, after the Protector's purge and the Great Fire in London where it was thought he perished, he was back again. Charles Stuart, the Boy King, had returned.

"He walked up to Angus and took the cross away from him, just like that. He didn't burn, and he didn't shy away from it, and it sat in his hand as if it was the most natural thing in the world.

"'Here,' he said, and threw it at the ground at my feet. 'Now I'll show you how a king deals with his subjects.'

"And before I could move, he lifted Angus off his feet and, with one lunge, his teeth tore a gaping hole in my brother's throat, the blood gushing black in the moonlight.

"I believe I roared, a shout of defiance, and I rushed him, my sword raised. He didn't even drop my brother as he backhanded me across the face as if he was swatting a fly. The next thing I remember is lying on my back staring at the stars, some ten yards away from where the shadows were butchering my brother. I managed to twist my head and look towards them. They were standing in a ring, and between them they were throwing what looked like a bundle of rags, a bundle that was getting increasingly smaller as they each took a chunk of it. It was only as the bundle finally fell to the ground, a mass of blood and gore, that I realised it had once been my brother.

"I tried to sit up, but something had busted inside—ribs, I think—and when I coughed there was a bubble of blood at my lips. There was a searing pain down the side of my face. Something, either his nail or a ring I hadn't seen, had ripped my face open here," he said, tracing the line of the scar from eye to chin. "And I could feel the heat of the blood running down through my beard.

"Suddenly there was someone standing over me. The Boy King ran a finger down my wound, gently parting the skin and drawing a fresh burst of pain, then sucked his finger clean of the blood that had gathered there.

"'You shall be my witness,' he said. 'What I begin here tonight is my destiny. You will see, and you will tell, and the world will know my purpose. Watch.'

"That's all he said, just that one word, but suddenly I could not move any of my muscles. I was like a statue, a mute witness to what happened next."

Campbell stopped again and stared deep into the fire, lost in his memories. Martin realised that the man's story held them all in its thrall—even Barnstable had given up all pretence of disbelief.

All of them took a draught from their ale—drinking had been forgotten since the story began.

There's not a great deal left to tell," said Campbell. "I believe you can guess his intentions. He raised the old red and white standard of the Stewarts, and an army of over a thousand Others roared and cheered, their screeching sending the night birds scattering over the sky. He proclaimed himself King, calling for Scotland to rise up to his banner and help him reclaim the old bloodline.

"And when it was over, he spoke to me once more, but this time his face was flushed and his eyes never left the trickle of blood by my lips.

"'Bear witness to this night, my friend. I go to Scone to be crowned on the old stone, but after that I head south. Tell them I am coming. It won't make any difference if they know in advance.'

"And while I lay there they left, almost as quickly as they had come, having turned over half my clan to their undeath, and having killed all others except myself and my daughter, who I found cowering in the church once I was finally able to move.

"It was a vile morning as dawn broke. Forty people I buried that day, including my brother. I said the rites as well as I can remember, and I did the things you have to do to stop them coming back. I pray to God it was enough. This cross I took as my own as you have seen.

That evening we slept in the church, and, at first light next day, we left, never looking back."

"And that is my story." Campbell said. "Do with it what you will."

There was a stunned silence before Martin finally spoke.

"But that was more than two months ago. Where are they? And what took you so long getting here? And what is wrong with your daughter?"

Campbell laughed and his eyes flashed and it was as if a gloom had been lifted from the room.

"All good questions lad, but I will only answer the first. My daughter's illness is a great mystery, and we were slowed down considerably by my injuries, amongst other adventures, but as to why they have not yet come, you could answer that yourself if you thought about it."

Martin was still puzzled, but saw that the Thane was nodding his head.

"Yes. Of course. They are waiting for the long dark nights—it gives them more time for their deviltry."

"Aye," said Campbell. "And all this time he has been building his army. On my journey I heard tell of whole towns being turned over. And don't think it is only the Others you'll have to contend with. There are plenty of men still alive who will have joined to his cause—the call of the bloodline is still strong."

"Now that I do not believe." Barnstable said. "True men would not debase themselves in that way."

"I can see that you have a good Christian community." Campbell said. "But there are many who have turned from our Lord, and the Devil is always persuasive."

"That is true," said the Thane. "And there are many Stuart sympathisers even on this side of the wall, though I have never really understood how such a sympathy arises. It is almost as if they cannot live within the Protector's strictures, and that anything else is preferable."

"Rebellion and the lure of endless undeath has a dark hold over many minds," Campbell said. "Who does not want to live forever?"

"Yes, but at what cost?" the Thane said and sighed deeply. "The time for waiting is passed. William, I need messengers sent, to Durham and Carlisle at least. And I need volunteers to go over the wall—we must determine their actions if we are to hold them back."

The Constable looked up from the fire for almost the first time since Campbell had finished his story.

"You cannot ask our men to go over the wall. That would be suicide."

The Thane clasped the big man on the shoulder.

"Have faith, old friend. This man here, alone, and with a sick girl, survived for months," the Thane said.

"But he had passage from the Boy King. I'm telling you now—none shall go." Barnstable said, and for the first time in his life Martin saw fear in the eyes of the big Constable.

"I will go," Martin said. Quietly at first as if to himself, then louder, and with more conviction. "I will go over."

He saw the sudden surprise in his father's face.

"As your Thane I am thankful and proud of my watchman," the old man said, standing to embrace Martin. "But as your father I would wish this task on some other man's son."

"With your leave, Sir," Campbell said, "I will go with your son, and look after him as my own, if you would do me the honour of protecting my daughter?"

"You have my oath on it," the Thane said, and the two men shook hands. Martin felt his life change at that moment, as if symbolically he had already parted from his father, some responsibility being passed in the handshake.

The Thane turned to Barnstable who was pushing himself out of his chair, slowly, as if he had suddenly become old and enfeebled.

"See to the messengers, William," the Thane said. "They must depart within the hour."

Barnstable left slowly, and it seemed to Martin that he was glad to be out of the Scotsman's company as if the bleakness of his story was somehow his fault.

"And I must go to write those very messages. See that our friend here is brought to his daughter," the Thane said to Martin. "Then come back. There are things to talk about before you leave."

Martin embraced the old man, and when he stood back they both had tears in their eyes.

Campbell clasped Martin on the arm.

"It seems we are to be travelling companions, young sir. Come, lead me to my girl. I am eager to know what your physician has made of her condition."

"As you should be," a voice said from behind them.

All three man turned to face the newcomer.

A small, wizened figure stood in the doorway. Every time he saw the doctor, Martin was reminded of the old legends of the enchanter Merlin. There was something about those deep blue eyes, the wild unkempt beard and the old, patched, clothes that spoke to Martin of magic kept hidden until it was ready to use. He had never spoken of it to the old man—he would have been roundly scolded for his efforts. Menzies was a man of science and the oldest man in the village— some said he was past his four score years, but Martin knew that he still had a mind like a steel trap, and no one for miles around, except perhaps for the Thane on a good day, could come close to matching him at chess.

He was also the man with the happiest disposition in the village, but tonight he wasn't smiling.

"She's bitten, sire, bitten deep."

The Thane turned on Campbell.

"You bring an Other into my house? At a time like this?"

"Aye," Campbell said. "For although she is bitten, she is still my daughter and I could do naught else. Aye, she is bitten, but she has not turned, nor has she shown any signs of doing so."

The Thane's anger had quickly turned to shock and surprise.

"Is this true?" He turned toward the doctor. "Two months bitten and not turned? Can such a thing happen?"

"Certainly it is true." Menzies said. "I have never heard its like before. But she is still a girl, and only a girl. The wounds have healed, but I fear that she has scars in her mind that may never be repaired."

"She must leave the castle," the Thane said. Campbell was about to protest, but was stopped as the Thane continued. "I will not break my oath to you, but there are people here, William Barnstable not the least of them, who would burn her first and worry about it later. We must send her away to a safe place."

Menzies was stroking his beard, a habit Martin knew from old—it usually happened just before the decisive move on the chess board.

"She may have a part to play in what will happen. There may be something in her blood that stops her from turning, and deciphering that trick is something the Protector would regard highly. There is a doctor in Sheffield I correspond with who has an interest in these matters. May I propose we send her to him? I can provide letters of introduction."

The Thane looked at Campbell, the question in his eyes, and Campbell nodded.

"But who can we trust to take her on that journey? It must be done in secret, for she will be killed quickly if she is found."

Menzies spoke first, and now his smile had returned.

"I believe I can help you there. Young Sean has not left her side since she was brought to me. He is over there now, stroking her hand and staring at her with big doleful eyes. I do believe the lad is smitten at last—maybe Shoreman can finally go away to work with an easy heart."

"Martin," the Thane said. "Will he do it, do you think?"

This time it was Martin who was smiling.

"I think you would have to tie him down to stop him," he said.

The Thane looked deep in thought, and it was long seconds before he spoke again to Martin.

"I am loath to go down this course. Already this night I have agreed to send a son away. I would not send another that I hold nearly as dear."

"He would go anyway, whether you willed it or not," Martin said. "You know his mind as well as I do."

"Aye," the old man said. "If it is to be done at all it must be done quickly. You must tell him the full story and get him out of the castle while Barnstable is busy organising the messengers. Then I think it best if all four of you leave at the same time. I can let the Constable think that I have sent you all over the wall."

He stepped forward and embraced Martin again.

"I will expect you back within a week. There are still things to say between us," his father said, then turned away, hiding his tears.

Martin and Campbell turned and left the room, one to say goodbye to a daughter, one to send his best friend away from his home.

CHAPTER 3

It was less than an hour later that the small group of five left the castle. They saw no one as they crept out, silently. It was easy for Martin and Sean to avoid the guards on the walls—after all, it was they who had set the timetable. They kept to the shadows and made their way quietly through the town, finally making their exit by a door near the South Gate.

The wind still howled, and the rain still came almost vertically into their faces, but Martin scarcely noticed it—he had eyes for only one person.

Campbell's daughter sat on the pony. Her face was uncovered now, and Martin could see what had so bewitched his friend. Her face was pale, but her skin shone like pearl in the moonlight, deep blue eyes staring out from under heavy lashes. Her hair hung in thick black tresses from her shoulders, and Martin wondered what it would be like to run his hands through it. But there was an emptiness in her eyes, as if her soul itself had departed, and she had to be helped onto the pony as if she was a newborn babe.

She stared listlessly ahead as Sean fixed her feet in the stirrups and loaded up the saddlebags behind her.

Sean had not left her side. He had listened to Campbell's story, albeit a shorter version of that told earlier, and had pledged himself once more to her protection.

"No harm shall come to her while I am alive," he had said, and Campbell had spat on his hand and they had clasped hands in the old manner to seal it.

Menzies had given Sean the letters of introduction, which were held in a leather pouch round his neck, and Martin had only enough time to retrieve his sword and his musket from the thankfully empty guardroom before Menzies was hustling them along to the stables to pick up the pony.

Now they gathered together one last time just outside the

gate.

"We could do with one o' yon ponies," Campbell said. "We may have a long trek ahead of us."

"No, no horses for you, I'm afraid," Menzies said, "They cannot be spared, for surely more messengers will be necessary in the days to come. Besides, I doubt if any of our animals would allow themselves to be taken over the wall anyway."

The old doctor turned to speak directly to Sean.

"The pony has her saddlebags packed with victuals for five days," he said. "That should bring you well nigh to Sheffield. Remember what I said: Jeffries is old—not as old as me, I grant you— but he is set in his ways. He may refuse to see you, but you must force him to read the letter. Then his curiosity will be pricked and you'll have his attention."

He was apologetic when he turned back to Martin.

"You, my lad, will have to fend for yourself. The castle cannot spare any more food without too many questions being asked. But I dare say your barbarian friend here knows the ways of the streams and forests."

"I was living on my wits before the lad was born, "Campbell said. "I dare say we will not starve."

Menzies stepped forward and clasped Campbell's arm.

"Take care of him, he shows promise on the chessboard and I would hate to lose such an opponent," he said. "Don't take unnecessary chances—we both know that the Others will come anyway, whatever we do in the intervening time. Do not put yourself in danger unless your life depends on it. And come back safe."

He turned and gave Martin a quick embrace, at the same time pushing himself towards the open door.

"Now go. Barnstable's messengers are due to leave within the hour, and you don't want to meet them on the road."

And with that he almost ran through the door, which closed behind him leaving them alone with the wind and rain.

"Which way will you travel?" Martin asked Sean, but Campbell stopped any answer.

"It is best that we do not know each others movements,"

he said. "In case of capture."

He didn't say whose capture, and Martin was suddenly struck with the enormity of the night's affairs. He had to fight down an urge to return to the door and pound on it until someone let him back in to safety and restored his old life to him.

Sean, as ever, caught his mood.

"As usual, we have things turned around," he said. "Who would have thought that you would be first over the wall while I ride south. We have got our adventure at last."

"Aye," Martin said. "But I have a feeling that it is you who are going into the most danger. Take care, my friend, for I have a pricking in my thumbs and a heavy heart."

"Never fear," said Sean, taking hold of the pony's reins and leading it away. "We will meet again. I feel it in my blood."

Martin shivered to fend off a sudden chill, and turned away so that Sean would not see his tears, and when he looked again his friend was already almost out of sight in the gloom.

He waved, and it was returned by Sean, and then the pony was lost from sight.

"He will make it to Sheffield," he said, more as a good luck talisman than through any great belief.

"Aye, I'm sure of it." Campbell said. "But what then? What then?"

Campbell shook his head as if to clear it.

"What's done is done, and she has gone on a path I cannot follow. But come, lad," he said, turning Martin's gaze to the north. "You must lead us to a path that will take us over the wall without being spotted."

Martin hadn't thought about that part of it. For the last hour he had thought of little more than being on the other side of the wall, with the Others. Now he realised that he had a task to perform before he even got that far.

"Which way do we go?" he asked, but the Scotsman shook his head.

"I came by the gate, remember? I know not the way from here. Until we get over the wall you must lead me."

Martin visualised the plan of the town in his head.

"If we go east," he said, remembering his watch with Sean from the night before, "There is a patch of wall that is crumbling and is low enough for us to cross. There will be a scramble down a gully on the other side, but that is to the good—it will hide our passage. Once down we will be nigh to the edge of the forest."

"Let us be off then," Campbell said, "For it will not be long before the sky lightens, and it would be best if we are out of sight of the wall by daybreak."

For once Martin was grateful for the wind and rain—it served to conceal them as they made their way up the steep bluff, taking care to stay low and out of sight of any watchman who might look south. Although Martin thought that unlikely. Tonight the watch would be keener than it had been for decades, and he doubted that a single eye would be turned in their direction.

As they approached the crumbled area of the wall, Martin motioned for Campbell to keep low and quiet, but there was no sign of any member of the watch. He began to climb over the wall when Campbell stopped him.

"Here," the Scotsman said, pulling apart one of the twin chains of garlic bulbs that adorned the top of the wall. "Fill your pockets with as many of these as you can—we may have need of them later."

Martin complied, even stuffing a dozen bulbs under his shirt against his skin.

They made sure that the remaining chain was whole and secure and, scrambling over it, went further than Martin had managed in his life so far—they were on the north side of the wall.

He stood there for a long moment, looking back at the wall he had spent so long patrolling. From here it looked smaller, less significant. It did not look like something that would stop an army. When he turned to share his thoughts, he found that the Scotsman was already making his way down, away from the wall. Martin had one last look south before following.

The gully was steeper than it had looked from on top, and Martin soon found himself scrambling in the dark among wet stones and slippery moss. His ankle turned over one larger stone. He fell, hard, and let out a small yelp of surprise. He was trying to stand when Campbell's face loomed above him.

"Would you at least try to make less noise," Campbell whispered. "We are supposed to be leaving quietly, are we not?"

Martin's face flushed hot, and he was glad that the Scotsman wouldn't see his embarrassment in the dark. He took hold of the man's proffered hand and pulled himself up.

"I'm sorry, I—"

Campbell stopped him with a hand raised to his lips and motioned for Martin to follow him further down the slope.

Even though he had looked down into this gully almost every day of his life, Martin realised as they descended that he had no idea where he was, nor how far they still had to go before they reached the flatter land beneath the outcrop. The forest butted up hard here and they would be in amongst the trees within a hundred yards of getting out of the gully, but in this darkness, Martin wasn't even sure about getting that far.

Suddenly his feet slipped out from under him again and he tumbled, first into a small stream that immediately soaked through every layer of his clothing. Then, when he was trying to regain his balance, his foot slipped on a layer of moss and sent a large boulder tumbling ahead of them which, as it rolled away into the darkness, brought a small avalanche of scree scurrying after it.

High above them on the wall someone shouted, immediately followed by the loud crack of a musket at the same moment as Martin felt something tugging at his left forearm, and looked down to see the blood already starting to seep from a wound. He felt around it, and was glad to note that it was only in the flesh, with no sign of a musket ball lodged there. There was, however, a lot of blood.

The shouting was getting louder, and within ten seconds more musket shots followed.

"It seems like your English hospitality is all that I

expected of it after all," Campbell shouted from somewhere below. "I suggest that we make haste down this slope—it wouldn't do to get ourselves killed before we're even out of sight of your home."

Another musket shot rang out, and that decided it. Campbell headed the way down and Martin followed, only just able to see the bulk of the Scotsman moving away down the slope.

More shots were fired, but the watchmen had lost them in the gloom and they were only wasting ammunition. Martin would have to have a word with them about that tomorrow...he stopped himself in mid thought. There would be no tomorrows, not back in Milecastle at least.

His thoughts had distracted him from what he ought to be thinking about, which was keeping his footing. Once more his foot slipped, but this time on scree, his legs flying from under him and knocking him down hard on his rear end. He fell hard enough to dislodge a fresh area of loose pebbles which collapsed, him along with it, and together they rushed headlong down the slope. He only had time for one shout of warning.

Campbell turned towards him, only his face showing in the dark, then Martin's flailing legs struck him and they both tumbled away into the blackness in a rush of stone and earth.

It seemed to Martin that they fell forever, but it was only a matter of seconds before they slowed as the land levelled out. The scree continued to rattle down behind them, and musket shots were following on behind it.

Campbell was pulling himself to his feet some three yards away from Martin, checking himself out for injuries, when a shot hit a rock only inches from him.

"Come on," he said to Martin, "We're not out of range yet."

Martin's arm had suffered further damage on the way down, and thick blood was dripping from his fingers as he stood. Somewhere back there he had lost his musket, but now wasn't the time to go looking for it.

Campbell had not yet noticed that Martin was wounded,

and was already walking away towards a darker part of blackness that Martin knew was the start of the forest.

Just then something small and white plopped down into the earth between the two men, then another. Martin bent down and picked one up. It was a single garlic bulb. They must have been using a catapult to get them this far.

And suddenly he was laughing, so hard that a fresh pain lanced along his forearm. He howled, a long low screech that he had learned years ago from Sean, and was answered by another volley of shots. He was still laughing when Campbell finally dragged him away, but the laughs had turned to sobs before they had even reached the forest.

"You're not going to lose your senses—are you son?" Campbell hissed, and Martin shook his head, but just then another bulb landed on the ground just in front of them, and the laughter rose again. This time Campbell saw the bulb, then they were both roaring and laughing, before Campbell finally dragged them into the relative shelter of the overhanging trees.

"You'd better have a wee word wi' your watch," the Scotsman said. "It seems they believe the bulb to be as potent as a cannonball."

"It may be they are trying to persuade the Boy King to laugh himself to death." Martin replied, and he could feel a manic giggling threatening to rise inside him.

"Aye," the Scotsman said, laughing "And it may be with those tactics they'll succeed. But come, let us not tempt them further." He led Martin further into the undergrowth.

Stray shots still rang out, but as they moved further beneath the trees their sound was muffled until soon all Martin could hear was the steady drip of water from the canopy. Even the wind was shut out down here.

After they had gone thirty yards in, Campbell stopped and turned to Martin. All Martin could see was the pale face seemingly hanging in the darkness, and he had a sudden attack of panic—had the whole night been a charade purely to get him out here? His hand was moving for his sword, but then the Scotsman moved towards him, and Martin could see the concern on his face.

"But you're hurt, man. Why did you not tell me?"

Martin lifted his arm and saw with dismay that the blood was still flowing and that his sleeves were sodden with the heavy red liquid.

"It's nothing, merely a flesh wound," he said, with more courage than he felt.

"Aye," Campbell said, "But there's some beasties in the woods that can smell blood a mile off, and I wouldn't be wanting to meet any of them on a dark night."

Martin started and began to stare around him.

"Surely they are not here already?" he said.

"No, it's not the Others I'm feared of." Campbell said. "They'll all be off to serve their Blood King—it's what they've been waiting for all these years. No, I mean normal, flesh and blood beasties. Some of them have thrived, even prospered, under the regime of the Others—bear have been found this far south, and there's wolves around that would chill your blood to see them. Pray that we never do."

Martin stood still as Campbell cleaned and bound the wound, and tried not to cry out as the bandage—made out of part of the sleeve of his shirt—was tied tight. His heartbeat pounded loud in his ears and in the muscle of his lower arm, but there was little pain and he was clear-headed.

Finally the Scotsman stood back.

"That'll have to do for now," he said. "But we had best be moving on—you've left a fair puddle, and a trail that a child could follow."

Martin looked down at his feet, amazed at the size of the pool of blood that had gathered there, and at the same time he realised that he could see Campbell clearly—at some point when his wound was being cleaned, the sun had come up.

He also realised that the rain, if not finally stopped, had eased to a light drizzle and, although water was still running from the trees and making its way down the back of his neck, it was definitely less than it had been.

"Aye, it's morning." Campbell said, seeing the younger man looking around him. "But we've a ways to go yet before

I'll be comfortable breaking my fast. Now, how do we get to the road without being seen from the wall?"

Martin was stunned to realise that Campbell was looking to him.

"I don't know," he said, "I've never been over the wall before."

"Come on, man," Campbell said, "Once we get to the road I'll ken where I am. But until we get there, it's up to you. You've stood up there and looked down often enough—you must be able to see for a good ten miles from there, if not more. Which way do we go?"

Martin tried to picture the scene in his head. From the wall the ground fell sharply away into the gully they had recently descended. They were about two miles to the east of Milecastle, and the forest was at its thickest here, a stand of birch and alder that stretched away north as far as the eye could see until it came up against a small group of hills in the distance. It butted up almost to the road, and to the west of the road there was a wide expanse of open moorland, wild heather and cottontail that stretched away to the sea some ten miles beyond. The road wended away into the distance, skirted the hills to the north that bounded the forest, and disappeared out of Martin's ken some fifteen miles away.

"We have to stay just inside the forest," Martin said. "From the wall it looks solid, with no way through, so I think that a direct route would take more time than we have. If we head west we will hit the road, but we have a good ways to go before we can safely walk in the open."

"Just what I thought." Campbell said, and sighed loudly. "I had hoped to reach relative safety by nightfall, but crawling about in the trees will take us most of the morning. We'd better be going. Lead the way."

Martin pushed his way through the trees, bringing fresh drips of rain on their heads. He headed west, keeping them just inside the tree line. Occasionally they would catch a glimpse of the wall and see small figures along the tops of the ridges, but there were no more gunshots.

The trees here were twisted and stunted and large hairy

mosses dripped from their branches to brush wetly against the men's faces. Everything that they touched or that touched them was damp and the ground underfoot was wet and boggy. Sometimes they had to skirt large pools, black, dank areas where flies hung thickly in the air. Once Martin thought he saw a flash of russet flank as a deer got out of their way, but there was no sound but the sucking of their boots in the mud. They didn't talk. Martin did not know what was in Campbell's thoughts but his own turned constantly to Sean, wondering just how far apart they now were.

After what seemed like an age, they approached Milecastle, the point where they had to go north. The gate was barely two hundred yards away, and the towers and turrets loomed over them. It had taken them the best part of the morning to cover that small distance. Martin looked up at the tallest turret and wondered if his father was standing there, already waiting his return. He fought off an almost overwhelming urge to step out of the trees and wave, just to see if anyone up in that tower would wave back.

"Come," Campbell said. "We must stay hidden in the trees beside the road for a while, but at least we will be heading north."

They headed onwards, and for a while he could feel the heavy stone presence of Milecastle brooding behind them, but soon all sight of it was obscured. Far to the west, between the trees, he saw that a thin mist was hanging over the moors, and a constant drizzle hung in the air. The ground beneath their feet was even more sodden than that in the shadow of the wall, and they soon had an inch-thick layer of mud on their boots.

They had been trudging in silence for over an hour when Campbell finally spoke.

"We can't go on like this—it is taking too long. We must take to the road and hope we aren't seen."

Silently Martin agreed, but there was another thought on his mind. "Not only is it taking too long, the rumblings in my innards tell me it is long past time to break fast. Curse Menzies—he could at least have allowed us one day's rations."

Campbell looked at him in mock surprise.

"Do you think I came out here completely unprepared?"

He took a small pack from across his back and, digging among the spare garlic he had stashed there, came up with a leather pouch about a foot long and six inches wide. Opening it up he removed several long thin strips of what looked like dried bark.

"Horse, I'm afraid, and dried last summer, but washed down with some forest water it should go down well enough. Beggars cannot always eat like kings."

Martin eyed the meat suspiciously.

"I had thought it only Frenchies who ate horse meat. I would expect anything of people who eat snails and frogs. But I took you for a more civilised man."

Campbell threw back his head and laughed, sending several crows out of the trees in startled flight.

"Rather horse than rat," he said. "Or are you trying to tell me that those were coney on the spit above yon fire in the hall last night?"

"Beggars cannot always eat like kings." Martin replied, and Campbell laughed at hearing his own words repeated.

Martin took a strip of meat. It felt as tough as old leather, but Campbell showed him how to tear strips off it without too much effort, and also how to get a drink of clear water from the thick moss under their feet. The water helped the meat go down and he was able to swallow several long pieces. He felt slightly less hungry ten minutes later when they stepped out of the forest and on to the road.

The first thing he did was look back, but Milecastle was hidden by the mist rising off the moor. He knew it was only a few miles way, but it seemed like much, much further. The road ahead of them was equally shrouded in mist and it felt as if they were alone in a vast gray, empty arena. Martin preferred the wind and rain—at least then you knew you were alive.

"Is it always this bleak?" he asked, and Campbell smiled.

"No—sometimes it rains."

Martin nodded his head, then suddenly realised he was

being teased.

"Here we are, "Campbell said. "Less than two leagues from your home, and you ask me about the prevailing weather? We are not in some wild foreign land—we have merely crossed a wall, an artificial barrier. The weather knows nothing of walls built by men."

In truth, although so close to home, Martin did feel as though this was a wild, foreign place. There was no sense of the pastoral here—no contented cattle or well-tended fields. He could not relax, not here.

"You mentioned a place of relative safety?" Martin asked, suddenly remembering the earlier conversation.

"Aye. But it is a long walk from here—nigh on twenty miles. We'll be hard pushed to make it before nightfall even if we run. And even then," he said, half to himself, "I'm not sure whether I would be allowed to find my way there again."

Campbell turned to Martin, and there was grim smile on his face.

"It looks like your first night over the wall may be spent in the open. Are ye ready for it?"

There was a knot in Martin's stomach, and he knew he couldn't blame it on the dried meat. But the future of his home might depend on him, so he nodded, and hoped that Campbell could not see his fear.

Setting their eyes to the north, they headed along the road, relieved to be finally rid of the overpowering trees around them.

"So where might this safe haven be?" Martin asked. "And how do you know of it?"

"It is an old place, from the time before the Bruce," Campbell said. "The people there know the ways of the Others, and have defenses against them. And they took me in when I was on the road to Milecastle. But I believe I'll say no more now—I don't want to spoil the surprise."

Martin knew by the grin on the Scotsman's face that he would get no more out of him on that subject. He chose to walk on in silence, his eyes continually trying to penetrate the fog, his body ready for any possible danger.

They walked for more than an hour, Campbell keeping up a fast pace that Martin, for all his youth, was hard pressed to match. The mist was thinning now, and they seemed to be climbing slightly. Through occasional breaches in the fog, Martin could see that they were approaching the foothills which marked the edge of his known world. Although they were still several miles away, he felt the thrill of going completely into the unknown.

"Where do we go when we reach the foothills?" Martin asked. "And what will we find there?"

"North-east for a while longer," Campbell grunted. "And the going gets rougher as we reach the higher ground. The old road which the Romans built leads through the dead burgh of Newcastleton, and on across a withered moor towards Dun Edin and the old castle on the high rock. But we will not be heading that far. I plan to reach Newcastleton tonight, then we will skirt the great forest and head eastwards towards the old abbey at Jedburgh."

Martin only had a vague idea of the geography on this side of the wall, and had only heard of one of the places Campbell mentioned.

"Dun Edin? Isn't that where the Old Protector finally caught Charles Stuart?"

"Aye," Campbell said. "Nigh on a hundred years ago, after the king of the Others had nearly brought your country to its knees. It was good for you that your Protector was so strong." He stopped, and there was a faraway look in his eyes. "But bad for Scotland that he didn't push home his advantage. He was back across the wall the very next day, taking Charles Stuart with him— back to London to face his public trial. If only he had pushed onwards—he could have ended it there. But he never caught the Boy King—and look at the trouble that has brought us now."

"I've never really understood," Martin said. "How did the Stuarts claim to have a right to the English throne in the first place, and how did Charles Stuart come to have a son? And how did the son grow to be the Boy King? And—"

"Enough," Campbell said, and laughed. "I'd almost

forgotten what it is like to be young and ignorant. Those are all long and bloody tales, whose origins go back centuries, but I will not tell them now, not here in the open where there are ears to hear. When we return to Milecastle you can pour me more of your father's fine ale, and I will tell you tales until your ears fall off in boredom. But for the here and now, all we have to know is that the Boy King is here, he wants the throne his father once had, and our task is to find out what he is planning to do about it. Now perk up, our pace has been slacking while we waste our breath in prattle, and the sun is already passed its height."

Martin stole a quick glance behind him, then stopped completely and turned around.

The mist had risen, and he was looking back the length of the road towards Milecastle. It was dwarfed by the scale of the landscape around it, the deep green of the forest leading to the blue grey of the escarpments and on to the slate blue of the sky. The castle's turrets suddenly looked small and insignificant and, by stretching out his arm, Martin was able to cover the whole castle with his thumb. To either side of the castle he could see the wall stretching away into the hazy distance. He turned to say something to Campbell, but the Scotsman was already over a hundred yards away and he had to run to catch him up.

"Never look back," was all Campbell said when Martin finally reached his side. "It only makes it more difficult to go forward."

The pace Campbell was setting was, if anything, faster than before, and Martin found himself struggling to keep up, especially since the path was climbing ever more steeply. He could see the brow of the hill some way ahead and focused himself on getting there. He looked over to find Campbell smiling at him.

"Do you think you could beat an old man to the top?" Campbell said, and immediately broke into a run, gaining a few precious yards for himself before Martin realised.

Martin forced his legs into action. He had never been a sprinter—that was Sean's department— but he knew that he had the stamina for the longer effort. It was only last year that he had won the Milecastle to Carlisle run on the day of the summer fair.

The Scotsman was getting ever further away, but Martin refused to try at this stage to catch him—the top was over a quarter of a mile away, and the Scotsman would have to be a devil to sprint all that way.

With a hundred yards to go Campbell began to falter, and with twenty to go Martin was on his shoulder.

They crested the hill together and both collapsed on the side of the road, panting heavily. It was several seconds before Martin was sufficiently recovered to speak.

"You daft old bugger, you could kill yourself with an effort like that."

Campbell smiled.

"It'll take more than a gentle stroll like that to put me down. And it stopped you fretting for the road back did it not?"

If the climb had been a piece of subterfuge, Martin had to admit that it had worked. His heart pounded and his throat was dry, but he felt strong and alive and ready for the road ahead. He sat up and looked around—forward this time to the way in front of them.

Beneath them the hill fell away sharply, the road following a twisting path to its foot where it forded a small river by means of an ancient stone bridge. Beyond that the road vanished into the thick cover of woodland that stretched as far as the eye could see, up and over the larger hills beyond whose tops were still hidden in thick mist.

Campbell saw him looking.

"They say that in the days before the Bruce much of this land was cleared. Farmers plied their trade on these hills, and the forest was kept in check. There was trade with the lands south of the wall. And if you can believe it, people even tore down sections of the wall to build their houses. But the dark days after Bannockburn put paid to all that."

Martin stopped him.

"You have mentioned Bannockburn more than once.

What is it? Is it a place?"

Campbell slapped his head in mock exasperation, but his eyes were twinkling when he replied.

"In God's name, what do they teach their children in England? Do you know nothing of the history of the Others?"

Martin was embarrassed. "The Protector has decreed it illegal to speculate, or even think about them," he stammered. "Our history relates to England, and England alone."

"Aye," Campbell said, "And any defeat can thus be safely forgotten. When we come to safety tonight, I will start your education—I take it you are willing to learn? I would not want to be making a criminal out of you."

Campbell did not wait for a reply. He rose to his feet and headed off down the hill.

"Come," he said. Let us see if there are any fish that would like to become lunch."

Martin resisted the urge to have one last look back along the road and followed the Scotsman down the hill.

By the time he caught up with Campbell the man was already wading into the river and bending over a large rock. Martin knew that trick as well, and possibly better than the Scotsman.

Two minutes later he was proved right as he coaxed a one pound trout out from under a rock in a faster moving patch of water, and tossed it onto the bank.

Campbell cursed him for a lucky dog, but Martin knew it was more than luck—old Menzies had been a good teacher, and he had been a better pupil. Many times in his youth they had used this trick; the finding of a good size rock in flowing water, the tickling of the cold flesh of the fish until it lay quietly in your hand, and the sudden grasp, holding hard, that allowed you to tease it out from under the stone. Menzies had been good, almost magical, in his fish-catching prowess, but Martin's skill was not far less.

Five minutes later he had another, slightly bigger fish this time. When he turned to throw it to the bank Campbell was already there, a fire started.

They wrapped the trout in heavy wet leaves and placed it at the edge of the small fire. Martin noticed that Campbell had taken care to put up as little smoke as possible.

"Surely we're safe in the daylight," he said.

"Safe from the Others maybe, but there's other things in these woods, and some of them are mightily curious."

Martin eyed the woods warily, but he saw nothing but the trees, and the smell of cooking trout soon brought his attention back to the fire.

They ate in silence, and Martin believed that the fish was the best he had ever tasted. Campbell buried the remains after they had finished, and spread the fire's ashes over a wide area.

"Best to leave no trace," he said. He rummaged in his backpack once more, and came up with what looked to Martin like a skinned animal. He went to the river and bent over, and finally Martin realised what he was doing—he was filling up an animal's bladder with water. Martin also realised how ill equipped he was for the journey.

He had a flint and some dried straw for making fire, a small bag containing powder and musket load, and, in a pack over his shoulders, a thick cloak wrapped tight in a roll. Apart from his sword, and the garlic bulbs he had collected on the wall, that was it. Suddenly he felt naked without his musket and wished he had taken the time to retrieve it.

By contrast, the old Scotsman seemed to have everything he needed at hand. Martin believed that, if it hadn't been for the current situation, the Scotsman might even be said to be enjoying himself.

When he looked up, Campbell was already making for the road.

"How much further today?" Martin shouted after him, groaning as his earlier exertions in climbing the hill made themselves felt in his calves and ankles.

"About ten miles to Newcastleton. We should make it by dusk," the Scotsman said, and, crossing the bridge, they were once more on the road north.

They walked on, continuing uphill, the way harder now. Campbell did not propose another run, and in truth Martin did not feel he would have been able to raise even a trot. His wounded arm was throbbing in time with his heartbeat, and a quick exploration of the bandage showed it to be wet through, so much so that his fingers came away red.

"Campbell." He said, and the Scotsman stopped, "I think we need to tear another strip from my shirt."

The Scotsman tutted and muttered under his breath as once more he cleaned the wound. This time, before ripping another strip from Martin's shirt, he padded the wound with some moss.

"That'll keep it clear, and stem the flux." He said. "But we must take care to keep it clean at all times."

When Campbell finished, Martin rearranged his clothing. He was going to feel cold in the arms, but the wound was well bound.

"Thank you, sir," he said. "Even old Menzies would call that a job well done."

Campbell bowed slightly.

"I'll take that as a compliment." He said. "But come. The day is getting on, and we have far to go."

So saying, he started out once more at a brisk walk.

Eventually they were walking in mist again, having reached the higher hills. It was growing perceptibly darker around them. Time after time they seemed to have crested a hill, only to find another stretching away in front of them. Martin's legs were weary, and his breath was starting to hitch in his throat. Yet again his clothes were soaked through, and his boots squelched each time they hit the path. He did not believe he had ever been so miserable—not even in the aftermath of the debacle in the byre.

He realised, suddenly guilty, that he had given little thought to Sean. He looked backwards, as if he could see past Milecastle to the road beyond, but there was only mist and fog. He said a silent prayer for his friend, then, head down, continued the long trudge.

After nearly two hours, Campbell stopped to allow them a drink.

"About four miles to go I would guess," he said and

grinned at Martin's groan. "Don't worry— one more hill, then it's all downwards. I cannot promise you any comforts at the end of it either, but we will have shelter, and a fire, and if luck is with us, a coney to eat. Here," he said, handing the bladder to Martin, "you finish it, there's a brook at our destination— we can fill it up again there."

Martin drained the last dregs of water gratefully, and handed the bladder back to Campbell. Just as he was passing it over a movement caught his eye over the Scotsman's shoulder as something short and green and fast ducked behind a tree. Martin had an impression of a pair of deep green eyes that looked straight through him. He started, and grasped the Scotsman's arm.

"I know," Campbell said before Martin could speak. "They have been with us for the past half hour. Don't worry—I was seeking to find them, but it seems they have found us first."

"Who are they?" Martin asked, but Campbell put his finger to his lips.

"Friends. Friends who are very shy, very careful. They will show themselves when they are ready."

They started walking again.

"And ignore them, if you can," Campbell said, seeing Martin scrutinising the area under the trees. "They can hide better than you can see anyway. Watch the road. Tell me of your life in yonder castle if it'll take your mind off it."

Martin started, hesitantly at first, but then he found that he was pouring out the story of his life: his mother dying giving birth to the lifeless body of his young sister, his friendship with Sean, and slowly, cautiously, editing out the parts which would make him look worse, the story of the affair in the byre.

Campbell laughed uproariously at that, and Martin thought he saw a flicker of green in the trees to his right, but he said nothing of it.

He continued with his story, telling of his affection for Menzies, and his hopes and fears for the Thaneship that would be his one day. He surprised himself by bursting into tears, and wiped them away guiltily with the back of his hand.

Campbell laid a hand on his shoulder.

"We will return soon," he said. "And you can show me your wall and your castle, and, yes, even the byre, or what's left of it. But look," he said, "we have conquered the hill."

Martin looked up. It seemed that he had been staring at his feet forever, just concentrating on putting one in front of the other. He had not realised that the incline had become less, nor that the countryside had opened up below them into a panoramic view.

The scene nearly took Martin's breath away. At some point during his monologue the mist had lifted once again, and the sky had cleared. Far to the west the sun was going down, a fiery, red ball that seemed to fill a quarter of the sky. He realised that he could see the sea, its surface red as blood as the dying sun sank into it and suffused it with colour. The sky was shot with pinks and purples, thin clouds scudding far overhead, their surface being caught and transformed by the last rays of sunset.

The hill was less steep on this side, falling away to a flat landscape that stretched as far as they could see, a plain that was all forest, its trees showing their autumn colours in shades of purple and brown and red. The road seemed to disappear into the wood about four hundred yards ahead, following the path of a small stream that gurgled and rumbled over the stony ground. Far to the east the silver crescent of a new moon was just appearing over the horizon, and, as if on cue, the clouds parted and the evening star blinked into existence overhead.

"I sometimes wish I was a bard, able to make songs to do justice to sights like this." Campbell sighed loudly. "But it is just another nightfall, to be feared like so many before it. Onwards, our destination is just down there," he said, pointing down into the nearer reaches of the forest. "And it's time we hid ourselves away for the night."

The darkness deepened as they descended, and Martin realised that he was trying to walk in the exact centre of the path, as far from both sets of trees as he was able to get. But there was no movement in the shadow, no sign that they were being followed.

At the foot of the hill the stream widened out and slowed, its noise no more than a murmur so that Martin suddenly became aware of the silence. So much so that he almost let out a yelp when Campbell ran off to one side.

"Missed it." Campbell said, returning, "A nice big coney that would have made us a fine supper. Never mind, there'll be more. Come on. Shelter is just ahead."

It was almost full dark by now. The path widened here, and Martin was aware of dark heavy shadows looming over them on either side, their shape too regular to be trees, but looking oddly broken and askew if they were the houses that Martin guessed them to be.

They moved up an alley of these shapes before Campbell stopped them in front of a tall building. Martin looked up to see the outline of a cross against the sky as Campbell led him forward into the ruined church.

In some ways it looked like the church had been vacated only yesterday. A white cloth still hung over the altar, and the sepulchral silence that Martin associated with these places still rang in the air, but when Campbell lit a candle taken from the vestibule, it was apparent that the building had seen better days.

Pigeon droppings littered the floor and mingled with the rotted straw and mud that had collected there. Above the altar, a huge figure of Christ on the cross was badly disfigured, his face hacked away, leaving only a deep black hole that swelled and shrank in the shadows and followed their every move.

"This is a Catholic church?" Martin asked.

"Aye. It was at one time. Some people preferred to take their chances with the Others rather than conform to the Old Protector's view of Christianity, and some of them ended up here, nearly ninety years ago."

Campbell looked around him and shook his head sadly.

"And they nearly made it too—but the Boy King found them during his first attempt at insurrection, and by 1665, all that were left here were the bats and the memories."

He knelt by the altar and crossed himself, muttering a prayer under his breath.

Martin was shocked.

"You are a papist?"

Campbell laughed, the echoes booming around them.

"By upbringing but not by choice. It is a long time since my last confession, and I do believe it would now take too long for me to tell. I was just trying to do something to remember the brave people who died here. You have no need to fear: I'm not going to sprout horns—or fangs for that matter. Besides, I prefer the term Catholic."

Martin looked up at the image of Christ above him, then immediately away again. The portrayal of suffering, combined with the black emptiness of the face, said nothing to him of the Christ he knew. He turned his back on the image.

"Start getting together some wood and get a fire going," Campbell said. "I'll see if I can catch us some supper."

Once more Campbell rummaged in his backpack, and came up with some long sections of thin cord.

"My snares," he said. "They served me well two nights ago, and the land then was less promising than this. Let's hope they do as well tonight."

He left, and the silence fell heavily on Martin. He busied himself collecting dry wood and straw and, once the fire was going, he sat and stared deeply into the flames, trying to ignore the flickering features of the face which loomed over him.

His body was all aches and pains, not the least in his legs where the muscles had knotted and twisted and were as hard as nuts under the skin. He bent to massage them, only to bring a new, flaring, pain to his left arm.

"Shot at, wounded, fell down a gorge, soaked to the skin and being followed by I don't know what, and it is only the first day," he muttered to himself. "I wonder what delights await me tomorrow?"

He lifted his arm and studied the bandage under his shirt. The whole thing was stained red again, made darker by the flickering firelight. Tearing another piece off the tail of his shirt, he rebound the arm, noticing with approval that the moss Campbell had put there was doing its job and the wound was still clean.

Shadows flickered at the edges of his vision, and he jumped at every small movement. He had re-stoked the fire twice before Campbell finally returned with a brace of skinned and gutted coneys.

"Fresh water and wild coney. A feast fit for a king—or two travelling gentlemen, at least." He held the rabbits up "I cleaned them outside and dumped the rest far downstream— we don't want any unwanted guests snuffling around during the night."

He placed the coneys on makeshift spits over the fire and sat down opposite Martin.

"And how do you like my homeland?" the Scotsman said.

Martin shrugged.

"I don't know what I expected. Maybe dark lords in high castles, shrieking hordes of Others screaming through the night. Certainly not this—it is almost idyllic."

Campbell snorted.

"There are still things abroad in the night, and we must always be on our guard. But if it's dark lords in high castles you want, there are plenty of them further to the north, but you had better pray you never get to see them—they are not places for Christian men."

The smell of roasting coney was making Martin's belly rumble and complain, but it would be a while yet before they were cooked.

"Tell me the tale of Bannockburn," he said. "It will stop the hunger from gnawing at me for a while."

Campbell looked into the flames.

"It is a dark tale, and the start of all our woes. Possibly you have heard of the Bruce?" Duncan said, and the mischief was back in his eyes.

"We are not completely ignorant," Martin replied, but Campbell was already continuing.

"He wanted to be king, to rule Scotland, but Edward of

England had other ideas. There were many battles, over many years. Wallace showed the Bruce the way, and was cruelly tortured and killed for his troubles. Maybe if he had lived things would have gone otherwise with the Bruce. We will never know.

"It all came down to one final battle, the lines drawn on a field beneath the old castle at Stirling, next to a small river—the Bannock Burn. Edward was confident—his armoured horsemen would surely be more than a match for the kilted horde of foot-soldiers that Bruce had amassed. But Bruce was a tactician and had led Edward's army into the trap—a deep mire in which the horses floundered and the armoured troops were unable to stand.

"Even then things were not going Bruce's way, for Edward's force were disciplined and well trained, whereas the Scots fought in small, clan-based groups with little cohesion or tactics. The English archers merely had to stand off and fire flight after flight into the mass hordes of the clans. Many of my ancestors died that day, as did many heads of other clans. In reality, it was to be the last day of the old ways. And while the arrows fell, it looked like the day would be Edward's.

"But as dusk fell, Bruce played his master-stroke, the result of a pact he had made three nights before.

"Some say that he stood upright in his stirrups, his face terrible to behold, as he took the choice between the devil he knew and the king he would not bow to, but I believe he knew all along what the result of his action would be. It didn't matter to him. He would be king, and his subjects would be just that—subject to his will, or whim.

"They came from the hills, only thirty of them, but their eyes blazed red and their horses were like creatures from hell itself, their iron clad hooves sparking fire off the rocks as they fell on their enemies. They were like shadows from hell, a black cloud that swept all before it. And where they passed, they left a bloody swathe of terror, a carpet of dead, dying and those about to be reborn. And men fled from the sight of the dark demons, the demons who carried a red cross on their white tunics.

"Templars they had been, but it is said they had made a bloody pact with devils under the Temple in the Holy City, a pact that gave them dominion and power. And power they had, for two centuries and more, but they over-reached themselves in France, and the king there expelled them and the Pope declared a holy war against them. Bruce gave them sanctuary, in return they gave him aid against Edward and protection from his enemies.

"And even as the dark horde was sweeping down on him, Edward would have stood his ground, but the sight that sent him and his army fleeing the field of battle was that of his soldiers, his dead soldiers, arising from the dead and marching down that hill towards their former allies.

"Edward and his army returned south to reinforce the wall, and an English army was not seen in Scotland again until the Protector came north after Charles Stuart more than three hundred years later.

"As for the Bruce, he took the thirty Templars into his court, and named them Stewards, and the dark bloodline of the Stuart family was founded and their bloody reign of terror began. Within two years the Bruce was dead, and William, the high Steward and keeper of the bloodline, was crowned High King. The Others began their systematic take-over of the country, and many of the old clans, mine included, were banished to the islands to scrape a living on those barren rocks.

"There is more," Campbell said. "Much more, about how the bloodline began, how it is perpetuated, and how Charles Stuart came to claim the throne of England in the name of his mother Mary, Queen of Scots, but it will have to wait—these coneys are ready for eating."

Campbell passed Martin a spitted coney, its flesh blackened and charred by the fire, the meat sweet and gamy underneath. As they ate they tossed the bones back on the fire, watching the sparks rise up into the eaves of the church.

"How do you know these tales when they have been long forgotten in Milecastle?" Martin asked, tearing a hot strip of meat from the coney's flank, and almost choking as the heat of it hit the roof of his mouth.

"It is a matter of culture. The clans have tales which have been told since the old kings came over from Ireland, and new deeds are always added to the tradition by the bards who sing in our halls. We grow up with the songs, and they never leave us." Campbell said, then returned to devouring his coney.

Martin could see the escaping grease glistening as it ran through the Scotsman's beard, and reminded himself that he must bathe in the river in the morning before he started smelling too rank.

After eating, Martin lay back and stared at the high vaulting ceiling, its broad beams looking as if a boat had been upturned and placed on top of the building. Red and black shadows ran across the structure, and in them Martin fancied he could see pictures: of battles in a field of mud, of dark horses charging down a hillside, fire belching from their mouths and nostrils, and of ancient skeletons in threadbare robes standing beside a king, their smiles widening as they bent towards the man.

Campbell started to sing, a low, mournful lay in a language Martin did not understand, but it spoke to him of loss of home, and of wandering in far lands. The song went on for a long time, and even after it had finished the echoes of it rang around the church for long seconds.

"My mother used to sing that one. She taught it to Mary, in the year before she died," Campbell said. There was a tremor in his voice, and Martin could see tears glistening at his eyes.

The Scotsman turned his back on Martin and stood. Suddenly he really looked like an old man as he shuffled away, towards the altar.

"You get some sleep. I'll wake you for your watch later," he said.

The shadows began to darken on the roof and, sometime later, Martin slept.

He woke with a start, the echoes of some unheard noise still reverberating in the church. Thin watery daylight was washing through the remains of the stained glass window to his left, laying multicoloured patterns across the floor.

The noise came again, a scraping, as of someone dragging something heavy across the floor. He reached a hand for his sword, just as there was a small noise to his left. He turned that way, and found himself staring into a pair of deep green eyes, eyes which focused sharply on him as their owner sighted over a bow, the arrow aimed directly at his heart.

CHAPTER 4

28th OCTOBER, 1745 NEWCASTLETON

"Don't move, laddie," Campbell's voice said to his right. "He's friendly enough, but a mite edgy because he doesn't know you."

Martin let his grip fall away from the hilt of his sword, and opened his hands, palms up. He even attempted a smile, and was rewarded when the green-eyed bowman lowered the bow—only by a couple of inches, but enough to let Martin start to breathe again.

"I wouldn't make any sudden moves," Campbell said. "I've seen them bring down a deer at fifty paces, so I don't think he'd miss from there."

Martin studied his would-be attacker.

He was short. Martin reckoned he was only about five feet tall, but lithe with it, full of a nervous energy like a deer startled on a woodland path. The muscles on his arms stood out proud from the strain of holding the bow drawn, but he was as still as a statue. There was no tremor in his limbs, and he looked like he was capable of holding the position all day if necessary.

He was dressed all in green, a roughly woven tunic of heavy wool which reached his knees. His legs were bare and his feet were clad in a pair of soft boots made of animal hide, also dyed the colour of grass. The bow was short, no more than three feet long, but thick and supple, and there was a small forest of arrows stored in a quiver slung across his back.

His arms were also bare, and traced with a patchwork of finely crafted tattoo work in reds and blacks—scenes of hunting, animals running through woodland, arrows bristling in their flanks, and tall columns of stone standing proud against open skies.

Martin's first impressions had been right: the eyes were green, a deep emerald sunk beneath a high brow, almost hidden completely by a fringe of jet black hair that hung loosely against his shoulders. He was clean-shaven, with only the merest hint of a fine downy beard and moustache. The features were fine, high cheekbones, a chin that almost came to a point, a thin, aquiline nose and a small, thin-lipped mouth which opened in a smile to show near-perfect white teeth. Martin got the impression of something wild and feral, something barely tamed. There was something about this man that reminded him of Sean.

"I am with Campbell," Martin said, and was dismayed to hear the tremor in his voice. "Friend?" he said, and stretched out a hand.

"I am pleased to meet a friend of Cam-Bell," the woodsman said, but didn't yet drop the bow. He spoke with an accent Martin did not recognise, a soft lilt that was more like singing than speech, but there was a halting nature, as if English were not a language he spoke often.

"The men of the forest bring you food and wish you welcome. Feed your bellies and empty your souls." he said, and motioned at something behind Martin.

Martin turned, and saw the source of the noise which had woken him.

A small deer lay on the church floor, the flights of two arrows standing proud from its chest. There was little sign of blood, and a long line dragged in the dust on the floor showed that it had been brought in from the doorway.

"Thank you for the gift of food," Martin said, and the bowman's face lit up in a smile and he bowed his head twice before looking back up at Martin.

"Lennan wishes you well of it. May your soul be empty and your belly full."

This sounded like a formal greeting, but Martin was stumped as to how to answer—such a meeting was way beyond anything in his etiquette lessons. He decided to keep it simple.

"I am Martin," he said, and reached out his hand again.

The other man finally dropped the bow and unstrung it in one smooth motion. The arrow and bow were both put in the quiver and the string rolled around his wrist while Martin was still moving. The woodsman leaned forward and clasped Martin on the forearm. His grip was strong— there was a power in his arms that belied his stature.

"And I am Lennan. Well met, brother."

The woodsman looked deep into Martin's eyes, clasping his arm in an ever-tighter grip. Finally he seemed to see something that satisfied him. With a nod he released the grip and stepped back.

"He turned up about half an hour ago," Campbell said. "And insisted we take the deer. Though what we're going to do with it, I don't know."

The woodsman spoke, but it was nothing that Martin understood. Campbell seemed to follow it, though, and there was a long discussion before Lennan turned back to the deer and, taking a narrow knife from beneath his tunic, began to disembowel and clean it.

"Does he have to do that in here?" Martin asked, and Campbell smiled.

"He thinks this is our holy place. They always eat in their holy places. I wouldn't bother about it—from what I've seen of his people, they waste nothing, and leave no trace of their movements, whatever they do."

"But who, or rather, what, is he?"

"I do not rightly know," said Campbell. "But I think he, and his people, are the last remnants of the old Picts, the ones who were here before all of us. The coming of the Others has almost been a boon to them—we were slowly overtaking them and by the time of the Bruce we had cleared most of their forests. But now we have gone again, and the trees have come back. My grandmother told me of them—the little people of the forest—but I had thought they were only a part of children's stories until I met them, two nights since, about ten miles from here."

"But what about the Others? Are they in league with them?" Martin asked.

He didn't see the woodsman move, but he suddenly felt the prick of a knife at his throat as he looked down into the flaring, staring green eyes.

"I think you may have upset him," Campbell said softly. "An apology might be in order."

"I am sorry," Martin said, aware that at any second his throat could be ripped out. He knew that his life depended on his next words, but he had no idea what to say. He decided on the first thing that came into his head. "My belly is empty and my soul is full."

The pressure of the knife on his skin reduced slightly.

"We are not like them. We do not like them. Their souls have been tossed to the wind. We were here before the dark ones, and when the gods return we will be there when they are gone." Lennan said. He waved the knife in front of Martin as if to admonish him, then went back to his work on the deer.

"I would not voice that opinion again too loudly in his presence," Campbell replied as Martin checked his throat to ensure that no blood had been drawn. "They hate the Others as we do, but they have a magic that keeps them safe."

"Magic? There is no such thing," Martin said, and snorted. "Our Lord may have performed miracles, but no mere man can."

"And so I thought. But they showed me things that night that gave me cause to wonder. They know things that they should not, and they can do things that we cannot." Campbell scratched at his beard. "And how do you explain the Others?" he asked. "Surely they are magical beings?"

Martin flushed. "Old Menzies insists that it is a disease, a sickness of mind and body that could be cured in the right circumstances. He believes it is something in the blood, that gives longevity but forces the cravings for drinking it."

"Then he is not the intellect I took him for," Campbell said. "But you will see the error of that soon enough. I have seen them in action, remember? And I can tell you it is more, much more, than just a disease—they have power, and it is best not to forget that lest it causes a drop in your guard. But come, let us see if your new friend needs help with the deer."

It looked like the woodsman was far from needing help. The deer had been gutted, skinned and quartered, and a haunch was already roasting over the fire while the remains were folded into the skin and taken outside.

"Won't it draw attention?" Martin asked. "Will the taint of it not draw the Others? Or even those 'beasties' you warned me of?"

"Lennan is a woodsman." Campbell said. "He will bury the remains deep. Learn to trust him, lad. There is no badness in him. Can't you tell?"

In truth, Martin had already come round to that opinion. There was something about the woodsman that impressed him, and instilled the trust Campbell was asking for. Whether it was his strength and stillness, or whether it was merely the lack of guile in his gaze, Martin felt that he could quickly grow to like him.

Martin and Campbell watched the haunch and tried to ignore the rumbling in their stomachs as the flames licked at the carcass and the smell of cooking meat filled the hall.

"Do you believe that the Others are in league with Old Nick?" Martin asked. "Barnstable says that they are all warlocks, like all papists."

Realising what he'd said, Martin suddenly blushed and began to stammer.

"I didn't…I mean it wasn't…I was only…"

Campbell let out a deep bellow of laughter.

"Dinna fash yerself man," he said. "I know your opinion of Barnstable—I saw it in your eyes back in that big hall of yours."

Martin blushed again. He was about to protest, more for form's sake than out of any sense of indignation, but was saved further embarrassment when the woodsman returned.

"May your bellies be full and your souls empty," the small man said, and bowed from the waist.

"And may the stones always stand and the wind always blow." Campbell said.

Martin looked at him quizzically.

The Scotsman shrugged. "I don't know what it means, but it was what they always said to each other the last time we met."

"It is the way of our people," Lennan said. "The stones are our history and the wind is our now, and our souls are what we will be."

"And what about your bellies?" Martin said.

"A woodsman knows that you cannot have true happiness unless your belly is full." Lennan said, and laughed, a high singing thing that seemed to ring in the eaves of the church.

"But come. The swift one is nearly cooked, and we have things that must be shown. Lennan has come to tell you of the dark men," the woodsman said. "Cam-Bell has told me that you seek news of the Boy King. My people have sent me to show you what you seek."

"But how did you know we were coming?" Martin said.

"The wind is our now, and it talks to our souls which are our future." Lennan said.

Martin was about to ask another question, but Campbell put a hand on his shoulder and stopped him.

"I wouldn't bother, laddie," he said. "They think in a different way to us, and I don't think we can fully understand them."

From a pocket of his tunic Lennan took a small leather pouch, and from that he took a handful of what looked to Martin like dried herbs. There was suddenly a sharp odour in the air, assaulting his nose and bringing him to the verge of a sneeze. It was like pungent vinegar, or the salts he had seen Menzies used to revive those who fell in a faint, and it was bringing water to his eyes.

"I hope that is not for dressing the meat," he said, but Campbell was smiling at him again.

"It looks like your education is about to continue. Watch, and say nothing."

Lennan tossed the handful of herbs on the fire, which flared briefly in deep blue, then started to smoke—small wisps at first that curled and twisted in the air as if alive, then great billowing clouds which hung in front of them and boiled in a great tumult.

Lennan invited them to sit, and Campbell seemed ready

to oblige him. Martin looked askance at the smoke. It seemed to coalesce and thicken, a rolling turmoil at its heart, as if there was something alive there that was desperate to escape. His heart thudded in his chest, and every fibre of his body was telling him to run, to escape from this thing that could only be the work of Satan, but to back away now would be to show cowardice, and the other two men seemed to be treating the sight as an everyday occurrence.

He sat beside Campbell, but was alert and ready for flight if necessary as the cloud thickened further, the grey smoke slowly turning blue, then green. The roof above them was now completely obscured, and the only thing Martin could see in the firelight was the flickering red shadows that danced on Lennan's face.

"What trickery is this?" Martin asked, but Lennan hushed him with a sharp glance.

"What I will show you has happened, is happening, and is yet to happen," the woodsman said. But Martin barely registered the sound of his voice—he was transfixed by the smoke, and the pictures which were forming there as the smoke cleared to reveal a moonlit scene.

It is night. A crescent moon hangs over a vast ruin, its stones fallen in a chaotic rubble, a moon that casts the stone in shadows of silver and black and grey. The ruin has once been an imposing edifice, but only a high tower remains, and on top of it stands all that is left of a cross, a jagged pinnacle of broken stone. Thick trees grow where monks once walked, and ivy has run over everything that remains standing. What was once a cathedral is tonight home to something monstrous.

Dark shadows flit among the tumbled stones, red eyes blazing like hot coals. They move so fast that it is almost impossible to believe that they were once men, but they have the requisite numbers of arms and legs, and they walk upright. They are dancing, a ritualised swirl around the centre of the cathedral, a celebration of what they are and what they are about to set out on.

There, in the centre of the ruin, stand eleven figures, somehow darker than the rest, and at first it is impossible to make out any detail in the shadows, but then the moon seems to shine brighter and it is possible to see that they are dressed in an outlandish manner.

There to the right is a tall thin figure in full battle armour from some centuries-old battle, the metal rusted and pitted, more red than silver. Over the armour hangs a tunic—once white but now a dirty yellow, only the red cross still vivid. It is only when you look closer that you see that the tunic is dripping, that the cross has been drawn in fresh blood. He carries a sword, a huge thing that is almost as long as he is tall. It is black and heavily scarred with the mark of many battles. He carries it in his hand as if it weighs no more than the smallest dagger. There is a visor lowered to hide his features, for which you are thankful, but red eyes gleam with a feral hatred through the grill.

Beside him is one who might once have been a monk, black robes torn and frayed, a heavy cowl pulled over a large head that looks strangely misshapen. This one holds a staff which at first looks like white wood, but on closer inspection seems to be fused bone. Human bone. The figure moves and the robe falls open, revealing a heavily built body that at first you take to be female. But then you notice the mutilated stump between its legs—a stump that exudes heavy drops of thick, almost congealed, blood.

The next is one who wears eagle feathers in his hair and has an overshirt composed entirely of ranks of old, thin, bones. He wears a skirt composed of hair, and when you look closely you can see the red, still bloody, scalps that the hair is attached to, which have been knitted together to form a crude belt. His face is painted with two red stripes across the large hooked nose, and his eyes are sunk deep beneath heavy brows. He smiles, and chipped yellow fangs slide from suddenly bloody gums.

A fourth is again something you have only heard of, never seen. His skin is yellow and his eyes slanted upwards at the corners. He is almost bald, but a long black plait hangs down his back from a topknot. He wears loose folds of cloth in golds and greens that seem to shimmer in the moonlight. His eyes, red like the rest, also show flecks of gold and silver. This one has fingernails so long that they curve round, almost back to his palms. The nails shine in the moonlight, and when he moves you can see that they are tipped in sharp points of metal.

The fifth is like a great bear, a huge figure clad all in black fur, his body hair so luxuriant it is difficult to see where his hair ends and his clothing begins. When the fur moves in the wind you can see that he is further clad in a tunic made of skin—torn, bloody scraps crudely sewn together, bits of it still raw and bloody. When this one smiles, he shows, not twin fangs, but a rank of yellowed, broken canines at least three inches long.

The sixth is female, but is only just recognisable as such. She is so old that, if she had been man and only man, she would have been dead long since. Her skin is folded and wrinkled with thin, flat breasts swinging against a bony chest. She is small, barely four foot high, and her hair is a tangled mass containing twigs and earth. She is wearing a necklace that, at first, you take to be horses pizzles, but then you have a closer look, and see that they are all too human, some of them still bleeding. She cackles as she lifts one of them to her mouth. Her fangs sink into the soft flesh and she starts to suck.

Four others at least look like something with which you might have some experience. They are dressed like Campbell, but the colours of their kilts and plaid have faded and worn. They all wear pigtails in the highland fashion, but you cannot imagine such as these laughing over a flagon of ale or dancing over their swords. Their eyes are dead, and when they smile, their fangs gleam white in the moon.

But your attention is caught by the one in the middle, a slim figure dressed in the highland fashion. No dirty rags for this one. His clothing all looks new and well tailored, making him seem somehow cleaner, less vile. His pale, aristocratic features shine in the moonlight, his skin seems to shine with an inner glow, and your eyes are drawn to his long blond hair falling behind him like a cape. This one, the eleventh and last, this is the one you have been brought to see, this is the Boy King come back to claim his blood-right.

He is not tall, and there is an air of studied mannerism about his actions that make him seem almost effeminate. Almost. But then he opens his mouth and the fangs slide from red gums. You look into his eyes and see nothing but death.

He surveys the horde around him and he smiles. And then you see the power in him—he raises a hand, and all movement stops, as if the scene has suddenly become a tableaux. But the clouds still scud across the moon and the shadows still lighten and darken. He holds the horde with his stare, then starts to speak, but you hear no sound.

It seems to you that a speech is being made, a call to arms. The fair one's actions become more forceful, almost frenzied, and the horde seem to sway in time with his words, until finally he releases them and they begin to cavort and dance once more.

A female walks through the throng, which parts to let her through. Your gaze is diverted from the Boy King for the first time. She is almost naked except for a few pieces of thin, gauze-like material. Her body, bone-white and like marble, disturbs you in ways you have never felt before, and her hair, blood-red, hangs to her waist, making you want to run your hands through it. You are so distracted that you do not notice the bundle that she carries until she reaches the Boy King and passes it to him.

The Boy King steps away from his companions, and his eyes blaze in crimson fire as the dance around him becomes faster, more frenzied. He raises something in the air—a child, a still living infant of less than a month in age. Its mouth is open, and its face is red, but still you hear nothing.

Something is said, and a darker shadow descends on the ruin as the Boy King bends his head. The child screams, and it cuts through you like a knife, the only sound yet heard. Blood gushes, black in the moonlight, and the Boy King's ten companions raise their arms to the sky.

You hear their voices as a faint chanting, but, even though it comes as if from a great distance, still it sends a chill through your bones. The scene widens, as if you have been raised higher above the cathedral ruins. You can see the countryside for many miles around, and through it all, along the overgrown roads and among the trees, shadows move, heading for the one who has called them.

The night becomes ever darker as the shadows pour in and around the ruins. The night is filled with dark things that had once been men and only men. There are thousands of them, and they are ready to die again to see the Boy King regain his father's throne.

Martin rubbed his eyes and shook his head. Had he fallen asleep? Surely these visions couldn't come to him when he was awake? But it didn't feel like a dream. The sound of the child's screams still seemed to echo around them, and Lennan sat, still and impassive, his head slightly bowed, those green eyes hooded in shadow. Campbell seemed to be in a daze, his eyes glazed and staring into a far distance.

Martin was aware of a harsh tingling in his nose and throat, and he was having difficulty breathing, but he could not draw himself away, as the smoke swirled and a new scene showed itself.

It is daylight, early morning. A thin mist is just beginning to be burned off, but you feel no chill. You are looking down, as if from a great height, on two people sleeping under a tree with a small pony tethered off to one side. Your heart gives a lurch as you realise you are looking at Sean and Campbell's daughter. They are lying side by side, for all the world looking like lovers after a tryst. Sean's arm is around the girl's waist and her head lies across his chest and shoulders. One of Sean's legs is crossed and entwined in hers, and he looks more settled, happier, than you can ever remember seeing him.

As you watch, he twitches, as if in a dream, and he pulls Mary Campbell even closer to him.

There was an amused snort from Campbell that dragged Martin's attention from the scene for a second. The big man had a smile playing on his lips, but he did not speak, merely motioned Martin to turn back and pay attention.

The smoke clears somewhat, expanding the view. You are rising upward again, the country opening up beneath you. At first it is exhilarating, like a memory of a childhood dream, but then you almost cry out as you see three figures, men and only men, two of them no more than boys, moving towards the sleeping pair. They are creeping slowly, taking advantage of the long grass to approach their quarry. One of them carries a musket, the other two carry heavy swords.

They look ragged and threadbare, and there is a hunger in their eyes, but they are certainly fit enough for their purpose.

Martin cried out, a startled exclamation that caused Lennan to turn and stare. He suddenly felt as if he had broken wind in church. But his cry seemed to have had an effect. There was a sudden movement in the scene.

Sean wakes with a start, and mouths a question. He raises himself off the ground and sees the approaching brigands, but too late. There is a muzzle flash, but no sound, as a musket is fired. Sean staggers and a blossom of red appears on the young man's chest. He falls to the ground, his body covering Campbell's daughter, whose eyes stare blankly upwards into yours as the smoke thickens once more and the scene fades as the brigands approach the prone bodies.

Martin made to stand.

"We must help them. He is shot, and will certainly be killed."

He felt a hand pulling him back to the fireside.

"Hush, laddie. Remember what the woodsman said—it might not have happened yet, and even if it has, there are two days and more of hard travel between us. We cannot help them. We each of us chose our path, and must follow where it leads. Come," Campbell said, and sat Martin down beside him. "It seems there is more left to see."

"No," Martin said. "There must be something we can do."

He turned to Lennan.

"He heard me. Didn't he? Sean heard me."

Lennan sighed, and there was such sadness there that Martin felt suddenly sorry he had spoken.

"Your soul called out to its friend and the wind carried your message to him. But my soul is full—it is too far a sending and we cannot aid him. But watch. As Cam-Bell has said, there is more yet to see."

Night again, and once more you are high over the landscape. The moon hangs over a jumble of wall and tower and courtyard that you finally recognise as Milecastle, seen from a vantage some two hundred feet above the highest point.

Although it is night, the people of the town are running around within the walls with a purpose you have never before seen. Extra barricades are being built, and you can see old Menzies scurrying around the town walls, directing the watch.

The patrols are out, doubled in force, on the walls. All eyes are facing north but they are unable to see what you can, the gathering of shadows in the gully that you descended the night before, the deeper blackness where the Boy King and his companions stand. The darkness seems to seethe around the gully, and there is the sense of a storm brewing, dark clouds that are about to break over the walls of Milecastle.

You see the Boy King move to the front of the horde, and watch as he makes passing motions with his hands in the air in front of him.

The air hums, the power palpable even at this distance. You watch, unable to turn your head away, as a guard, as if in a trance, reaches forward onto the wall and tears the chain of bulbs into shreds, strewing the herb far and wide. All along the line you see that others are doing the same. The men of the watch, men you have grown with and trained with, are betraying their duty and they can do nothing about it. The wall is breached before a single Other has fallen.

The Boy King slumps in the arms of the tall companion wearing the armour, and your heart lifts. He is tired, the effort he has expended in controlling the watchers has weakened him. He can be beaten.

But then you see the size of the army he has brought with him, and can only watch as it moves forward in a single dark mass.

You have tears in your eyes, but you don't know it, your heart transfixed by the sight of the black shadows pouring over the wall and down the hill, down towards Milecastle.

You see the men of the watch on the wall shake themselves back to their senses as the pale one's spell lifts from them, just before they are engulfed by the black tide.

Muzzle flashes light the sky and a shudder runs through the darkness, but it doesn't slow as it breaks against the wall and seems to defy gravity. It flows up and over to fall on the people below. A red mist suddenly hangs in the air, a mist that you know is the blood of your people.

"No!" Martin screamed, and, rising up, too fast for Campbell to stop him, he rushed headlong for the fire, as if attempting to dive into the picture.

And in the scene ahead of you, the greater darkness shifts, and the ten companions stop and look skywards. The armoured one releases the Boy King who stands upright and raises his head. You find yourself staring deep into the blood red eyes of the pale one. No words are spoken, but you feel the pull of the charm, feel yourself being dragged down, deeper down into those dark cold depths where he could tell you anything and you would believe him.

There is a ringing in your ears, and in the distance you hear a voice you know, a deep Scots voice that demands attention, that you know you should heed. But the eyes are too strong, and you feel yourself falling, falling.

A sudden pain in his left arm brought Martin out of the scene with an abruptness that left his head reeling. He looked down to see that Campbell had grabbed him by his wounded arm and was digging his fingers into the bandage, bringing a fresh flow of blood.

He twisted away from the Scotsman and turned back to the smoke, but there were no visions there, and already the green had turned back to grey and the rolling cloud was dissipating, wispy feathers scattering through the church and out through the doors.

Campbell dragged him off, away from the rapidly disappearing smoke, and Lennan dampened the fire down by spreading the ashes over a wider area.

Martin struggled harder against the Scotsman, but the man held him tight until the younger man finally relaxed.

"They have taken Milecastle," he whispered. "The Others are in my home, while I am out here chasing shadows. A fine officer of the watch I turned out to be." He turned away from Campbell lest the Scotsman see the tears in his eyes.

"You forget something," the Scotsman said. "It was full dark in the vision. Full dark and moon-lit. Whenever it was happening, it is not now"

The woodsman looked up from the remains of the fire, holding the spit carrying the haunch of the small deer.

"The grasses show what the soul desires, what the wind fears. Eat now," Lennan said. "Fill the belly and empty the soul."

And despite his worry over the visions he had just seen, Martin realised that he was indeed ravenously hungry, as if he had already done a full day's work in the field.

He felt saliva build in his mouth as Lennan sliced long strips of meat from the joint. The woodsman handed him a piece, and he devoured it greedily.

Between mouthfuls he spoke to Campbell.

"We must go back. God alone knows what has happened. You saw it?" he asked, suddenly worried that the visions were his and his alone, that he had suffered a malaise of the brain.

"Oh aye, I saw it," Campbell said. "But two nights ago I

saw myself being killed by two young fellows at the gates of Milecastle, and that did not come to pass—unless I am a phantasm and simply do not know it yet."

Lennan held up a hand and counted off on his fingers. "What was, what is, what will be. I told you this. The last has not happened, may not happen. Will not happen if the gods are with you and your soul is empty. Eat now. Fill the belly and empty the soul."

"But he saw me. He knew I was there," Martin said.

Campbell was staring into the smouldering ashes, as if to will one last vision.

"Aye, he knew. Or he will know, when the time comes—I do not pretend to understand the ways of magic. But I do know that I pulled you away at the right moment. The Boy King almost had you, laddie, and whether it is now or at some other time, that it not a thing to take lightly—he will know you now if you meet again."

"Aye," said Martin. "And I will know him. But I cannot believe this to be Christian. We are not meant to see what is yet to come."

"You haven't been reading your scripture," Campbell said. "Were not the prophets held in great reverence? And did Saul not consult the Witch of Endor?"

"Yes. And our Lord foretold what would come to him. But they are prophets and kings. We are men and only men." Martin replied.

"The gods give where they will, and of what they will. My soul is emptied." Lennan said, then turning to Campbell, continued, as if discounting the conversation as an irrelevance: "Your friend is right. You must return to the stone halls. First the gods showed us the site of the old holy place. That was two nights ago. I have word that the dark brethren are headed for your wall. It is right that you go back. Although what was seen may not be seen again, it would be wise to be prepared."

Campbell looked worried at this.

"If they were in Jedburgh two nights ago, they could be over the wall by now."

"They are not," was all Lennan said. "And you must leave

soon—the day is long started and it is a long walk for souls as full as yours. Come. I will lead you."

Lennan left the church, and Campbell made to follow.

"Wait," Martin said, "What about the rest of the food?"

"We will be travelling fast and light," Campbell said. "And it may be that there will be no fires lit on the way. Lennan is a woodsman—let us leave it to him to provide for us. And unless you have a mind for raw venison, I suggest we leave it here. Someone, or, more likely, something, will have the good of it. Now come. Lennan moves swiftly, and he may forget that he is leading us."

On leaving the church Martin had to squint in the sudden brightness of the day, and was surprised at how high the sun was in the sky. The visions of the past hour were still fresh in his memory, as if carved there permanently. The sight of his home being overrun by the Others filled him with a deep rage, and he knew that he had to get back there fast, and make the necessary preparations—he wanted to be there, ready and waiting, when they came, if only to take revenge for the child he had seen die. But when he looked at the sky, and at the position of the sun, his heart sank.

"We will never make it by nightfall," he said.

Campbell too looked skywards.

"It is doubtful, I grant you that, but Lennan knows the ways of the forest, and may find us a more direct route than that by which we came. Come, it is time to move fast and talk little."

Lennan was already at the edge of the forest and was beckoning them onwards. Martin barely had time to register the tumbled ruins scattered around the church, the last vestiges left by men, and only men, who had tried to withstand the Others.

"We must go," Campbell said, and there was a new urgency in his command. "We cannot stand by and let your country become like mine."

"With men like you, we will prevail." Martin said, and clasped the older man's arm as they moved away from the ruined town. He said a silent prayer, vowing that Milecastle would not suffer the same fate, before he was engulfed in shades of green and russet as the forest closed around them.

He could not see any trail, but Lennan was bounding ahead, as sure-footed as if he was walking in an open field. Martin followed as best as he was able, and could hear Campbell lumbering through the foliage behind them. He was glad to be in the middle of the trio—there was less chance of him being separated from the others that way.

He felt like he was worse than useless out here, away from all that was normal to him— Lennan, a woodsman, would not be at home anywhere else, and Campbell was capable and self-assured. It was like being a young boy again when he had to learn the ways of the wall—there was the same feeling of helplessness and being out of his depth. All he could do was stay alert and hope he could be of help if any crisis overtook them.

The trees crowded around them. They were bigger here, down from the high ground—bigger, thicker and older, surrounded by an undergrowth of bracken and fern, with the occasional sapling trying to push its way up to the thin light coming through the dense canopy.

Leaves fell softly around them, a steady rain of papery brown that foretold the winter that was on its way. Martin fell into the rhythm of Lennan's stride, swerving this way and that through the trees, only struggling through undergrowth where necessary, but all the time taking the path of least resistance through the trees. He could hear a quiet piping noise ahead of him, and realised that Lennan was singing.

It was a glad tune, an air he almost recognised, and he hummed along as Lennan's voice spoke to him of open skies and starry nights, of running with the wind like a deer, of cutting through the sky like a great eagle. The forest seemed to sparkle with life, each leaf gleaming emerald, silver pouring through the veins, but he could not stop to look, for round the next tree, and the next, were more wonders.

There on his right was the tree that was over one thousand years old, the tree that grumbled and groaned as it tried to suck up moisture through roots that had gone tough with age. And there was the sapling that would usurp it one day, all brightness and energy and vigour. Down there among the undergrowth he could hear the small rustlings as fungi pushed their fruiting bodies towards the sky, and small animals scurried for shelter at their approach. A grey owl watched him impassively as he passed beneath it, eyes blinking in unison as if giving permission to use its territory.

Through wood, up hill, along riverside the song continued, and now Martin sang along for, although he did not know the words, he now knew the meaning.

His feet hit the ground in all the right places, not once finding a loose rock or a pothole or a root, and his heart pumped, slow and steady although the ground seemed to race by. And once, on a hilltop, with only blue sky above, he held the song alone while Lennan watched and smiled.

As he sang, he felt the wind in his face, a clean breeze that washed away the memories of the church and the scenes in the smoke. Instead, he found himself thinking, for the first time for many years, of his mother.

His last memory of her was from a day like this. He had been seven years old. She was watching as Sean tried to teach Martin how to tie a hook to a fishing line. The younger boy had managed it with ease, but Martin found himself all fingers and thumbs, and was getting rapidly red-faced in frustration until Sean laughed, and Martin lashed out, hitting his friend across the cheek, raising a welt.

The boys had squared up to each other. They had never before fought, and Martin wished he could take the blow back, but there was a look in Sean's eyes he would come to recognise in later years, and he knew the fight would be hard.

And that was when his mother had screamed. The last sight Martin had of her was when as the midwifes gathered around her and carried her off, leaving only the red stain of her blood on the grass.

Martin's song faltered and faded, and he fell to his knees, sobbing now.

"Your souls did not fight, only the wind between you," Lennan said. The little woodsman was still and grave, and when Martin looked up through his tears he was reminded of a churchman delivering a sermon. "Her soul does not feel that wind, only the souls and their friendship. It is through your friendship that her soul is cleansed. Empty your soul and she will be content."

The woodsman held out a hand. Martin took it and he was pulled up as if he was as light as a feather. As he stood he realised he felt cleansed, as if a weight that had been with him for a long time had suddenly been lifted.

Lennan smiled.

"She has emptied your soul."

He turned away and began to sing again as he led them down from the hill.

Still they walked, through patches of wood so dense that it seemed night had fallen early, over open moorland where the grouse fluttered from beneath their feet, until they reached a hollow, a natural amphitheatre near the top of a tall hill.

The trees had been deliberately cleared here, for there were ancient stumps covered in moss still sticking up from the boggy ground. The sun shone from a clear sky, and the air felt cold and thin and pure. High overhead a buzzard screeched its hunting call, but then all was silent, not even a hint of a breeze disturbing the calm. The sweet, almost sickly smell of heather blossom hung heavy in the air.

Lennan stopped, and Martin almost collided with him before, with an effort, he managed to still his body and stand quiet. Campbell joined them, and Martin noticed that all three of them were smiling broadly.

"Our souls are empty," Lennan said. "And we have travelled well. Six leagues we have come, and look, the sun is at its highest. Let us give thanks to the gods."

Martin looked to Campbell.

"Six leagues? But surely we have been walking less than an hour? I feel no tiredness."

"It is the magic you do not believe in again," Campbell said, smiling. "Look at the sun—we have been walking for hours."

Martin looked around him for the first time since the

song stopped. It was true that the sun was high in the sky, but his body did not believe it—he wasn't tired, there was no sense of any muscle strain. He did however feel hungry again.

He looked around once more, wondering where Lennan had led them to, and saw the woodsman heading towards the centre of the amphitheatre, to the small ring of tall stones that stood there.

Martin followed Campbell as they went to join him.

"What is this place?" he asked.

"It is one of the old places," Campbell replied. "Circles like this can be found all over the country if you know where to look, but the use of them has been lost in time. But watch—I believe our new friend will show us what it is for."

The stones towered over the men, the tallest of the group of five being nearly ten feet above their heads. It was rough-cut, as if hewn directly from a cliff, and its surface was covered in carvings that mimicked the tattoos on the woodsman's arms. Martin reached out and stroked the nearest carving, marveling at the intricacy of the work and the coldness of the stone even now, at the height of the day. When the sun shone on it the stone glistened, the minerals caught in it sparkling like stars caught in the surface. The woodsman also ran a hand over the stone, gently caressing it as if afraid it might break.

"Here the gods will take our thanks and our bellies will be filled again. This is one of our places, where my people worshipped in the days when our bellies were always full and our souls were always empty and when our gods walked with us always. Here the stars told us when the gods would come, and here we wait for the gods to come again," Lennan said. "And here, the gods can still bestow their gift of food to us."

He stood in the centre of the small circle and raised his hands high above his head. The air seemed to sparkle again, and, from the moor at the rim of the amphitheatre, three grouse took to the air, as if startled by a sudden movement. Martin watched as they swooped around above them. Out of the corner of his eye he caught a quick movement and saw Lennan clench, then unclench, his fists, just once. The birds fell out of the sky as if shot, dropping dead at the woodsman's feet.

"Our thanks to you," Lennan said, addressing each of the stones in turn. "Our souls are empty."

He lifted the birds and, without another word, began to clean them, preparing them for cooking.

Martin stood and stared, not quite believing what he had just seen.

"Close your mouth, laddie," Campbell said to him. "The woodsman didn't cause the flies to fall, and you don't want to be catching them."

"Did he...?"

"Yes. He did. Come on," Campbell said. "We'd best get a fire going—it looks like food has been provided."

It looked like more than food was provided. By the side of the stones was a stack of dry wood, and a ring of boulders where fires had been set in the past.

"This magic of the woodsman is not natural," Martin said as they stacked the wood on the fire.

"On the contrary, I think that's exactly what it is," said Campbell. "They know the ways of the wild, and the wild provides for them. Their magic would not work if linked to a hearth and home, town and castle."

"But the Lord does not give us food on demand—that is too easy."

Campbell chuckled.

"I suspect that the woodsman's magic has little to do with our Lord. They have been in this land since before Christ, probably even before Moses. But have you forgotten your prayers? 'Give us this day our daily bread' Is that not what we ask? The only difference is that the woodsman's gods seem to answer."

Martin was about to protest when he realised he was being teased.

"I still don't like it," Martin said. Just then Lennan brought the birds to the fire, so the conversation was concluded. Campbell seemed eager to get to the food and had his back to Martin, so Martin's companions didn't see him turn his ankle in a rut on the ground. Nor did they see him hit his wounded arm against the largest stone as he tried to regain balance.

None of the three companions saw the smear of bright red blood which was left there as Martin went to join them, limping slightly as he walked.

Once more they were gathered around a fire, once more waiting for food, but Martin was thankful that there was no repeat of the morning's performance. Lennan sat in silence, only occasionally moving to turn the birds.

"Where are we?" Martin asked.

"I have told," Lennan said. "A place of our gods."

"Yes," said Martin. "But how much further to Milecastle? And how long will it take us to get there?"

"The stone town is ten leagues to the south west," Lennan said. "And it will take as long as the gods wish. Now fill your belly and empty your soul."

The last was spoken harshly, an admonishment to Martin's unbelief. They ate the birds in silence. Martin found them tough and gamey, but the others ate them heartily enough, and at least there would be no problems in removing pellets of shot. Soon all that remained was a small pile of bones.

"Our bellies are full and our souls are empty," Campbell said, and Lennan smiled broadly.

"And our feet will travel lightly on the path," he said. "Come, we must travel fast once more."

Lennan scattered the bones away from the stones, and doused the fire before they headed out of the amphitheatre. Although it was autumn, the sun beat down hard on Martin's head, and his stomach felt full and swollen. He was a long way from the contentment he had been feeling that morning, and this time, when Lennan began his song, it was only that, a song, and Martin felt no compulsion to join in.

Campbell and Lennan were both singing now, and they were striding away over the moorland. To Martin it seemed that their feet were not touching the ground, so lightly did they travel. He was having to walk ever faster just to keep up with them, and it was only when they topped the hill and began to descend that he was able to come alongside Campbell.

Martin was sweating heavily from his exertions, and his legs felt like blocks of stone each time he took a step. His arm was throbbing again, but he was concentrating so hard on putting one foot in front of the other that he failed to notice the steady drip of blood which ran from his wound.

Campbell was beyond noticing anything. He had a blissful smile on his face, and he was singing, his deep bass in counterpoint to Lennan's higher tones. His eyes stared straight ahead, never looking at his feet, but he still managed to avoid all the boulders, holes and roots that Martin's feet seemed determined to find.

Martin noticed that they were once more descending into thick forest. He looked over the treetops but could see no path, no sign of their direction, only more trees stretching as far as he could see. The forest closed over them, and this time Martin did not feel welcome.

His ankle had begun to pain him, and once more he found he was lagging behind his companions. He wasn't too worried, not yet—they seemed to be following a path of sorts, a trodden-down run, either made by the woodsmen themselves or deer. He tried to keep up the pace, to keep them in sight, but soon the trees closed in and the light got dimmer, then dimmer still, until he was following only the sound of the twin voices, still singing.

He had to rest. His ankle now hurt every time he put weight on it, and the wound on his arm throbbed and ached with every step. He was hot, and the humid air here deep under the trees seemed too heavy to draw into his lungs. He found an old rotted tree stump and sat down.

"Just for a minute. Just to catch breath," he promised himself. But by now even the sound of singing had faded in the distance, and Martin suddenly felt alone in the too quiet forest.

With the weight off it his ankle didn't seem too bad, but it was with dismay that he finally noticed that blood had been pouring freely from his wound. The sodden bandage was almost hanging off, and the left hand side of his tunic was matted and stiff where the flow had soaked in.

He stood, and found his head spinning—so much so that he sat down again, hard, to avoid falling. He sat for a long minute, waiting for the pounding at his temple to dull from an ache to a throb.

Slowly he bandaged his arm up again, using the last available piece of his shirt, and was just about to try standing again when there was the faintest of rustles from the undergrowth to his right. He turned his head that way and, for the second time that day, found himself looking into a pair of green eyes.

These ones were not human. They belonged to a wolf, a huge grey male that was beginning to get its winter coat— shaggy and pale around the shoulders, darker grey along the flanks. Its lips pulled away from its teeth, showing milky-white canines and a blood-red tongue.

The eyes continued to hold Martin in their stare as he stood, slowly, and began to back away, trying to release his sword from its scabbard.

As he backed off, the wolf moved towards him, pacing his movements, his eyes never leaving his. Martin's brain was working frantically, trying to remember all the lore he knew about the creatures.

He had never seen one before. He had heard them enough—all the men of the watch had, but south of the wall they had been eradicated more than a century ago. All he really knew was that they were bigger and stronger than the dogs the huntsmen of Milecastle kept, and that they were still used as objects of fear and terror in children's tales. He backed off further, careful to make no sudden movements.

He realised he was still holding the sodden bandage he had taken from his arm and tossed it in the wolf's direction, all the while backing away ever faster up the path.

To try and run would be futile. He knew that the creature would be able to outpace him, even if he was fit. His only hope was to keep his eye on it and hope it had a fear of an armed man. The thought struck him that here, north of the wall, it might never have encountered a man, armed or otherwise. Martin began to tremble.

The wolf lowered its head to the sodden bandage and sniffed it, then, almost derisively, pushed it aside with its nose and stared at Martin once more. It began to walk forward, slowly, still pacing him as he walked backwards up the path.

He was close enough to smell it, a heavy musky odour, nothing like that of his father's fox terriers. Its flanks moved with each breath, showing rippling bands of muscle, and thick drools of saliva hung from its jaws.

Martin prayed that his companions had already noticed his absence, would already be on their way back down the trail, but he didn't hold out too much hope—he well remembered the blankness of Campbell's stare.

He finally managed to get his sword out of its sheath, and waved it in front of the beast, hoping that it might retreat at the sight of cold steel, but it kept coming, following him remorselessly.

Summoning up what little bravery he felt, he took a step forward. The wolf stood its ground, the green eyes daring him to come closer.

Martin's legs were trembling, threatening to collapse beneath him. He had never killed, or attempted to kill, anything larger than a coney—that was more Sean's line. His friend would probably have dispatched the creature by now and be wearing its hide as a coat. That thought gave him a spurt of courage and he took another step forward, raising the sword before him.

The wolf crouched down on its haunches, preparing to spring, and, that moment, from far off to his left—but not far enough—came the long piercing howl of another beast, followed by an answering cry to his right. The wolf drew its lips back again to show its teeth.

Martin realised he had very little time—he had no chance against a pack. He stepped forward, swinging his sword down towards the wolf's head. The beast sprang at the same moment, and the sword caught it a glancing blow on the shoulder, not even slowing its attack.

Instinctively he threw out his left arm across his throat, just as the wolf's jaws clamped shut. Long teeth raked his arm, opening further the already bleeding wound, and the wolf went mad in a frenzy at the taste of blood.

Martin's sword was useless at this close range. He was unable to get enough room to swing it, and could not find sufficient angle to bring the point to bear. He hit the beast in the head, again and again with the hilt, but that only enraged it further as it chewed deeper into the flesh of his arm.

The weight of the creature dragged at him, threatening at any moment to pull him off his feet as they staggered together in a grotesque parody of a dance. They lurched left and right, and the pain in his arm flared and burned, threatening to overwhelm him.

He only had one option open, and it would leave him vulnerable to attack, but he had to try, his mind full of the thought of the rest of the pack.

He swung his left arm around, pivoting with his body, lifting the wolf off the ground, screaming aloud at the sudden, white-hot pain that flared in the wound. At the same time he lifted the wolf's head as high as he could, thrusting it away from him while bringing his sword around in an arc. He hit the beast in the side, biting deep, but his sword met bone and jarred, knocking it out of his hand.

The creature made a whimpering noise in its throat but hung on tightly to his arm and, as his swing turned him fully around, their combined weight finally sent them to the ground where Martin rolled and kicked and gouged—as wild as the animal that was attacking him.

The wolf was in a frenzy. It drew up its rear legs and began to gouge at Martin's jerkin with its claws. The leather was holding, but Martin knew it was only a matter of time before his belly was opened.

His strength was going fast. His arm was most probably by now a bloody ruin, and he could feel the fangs grating against his bones. It could only be a matter of seconds before the other pack members arrived. He doubled his efforts, one last push to try to get the animal away from him. And then he felt something move under his shirt. He managed to free his right arm just long enough to remove a long forgotten clove of garlic and, crushing it in the same motion, thrust it into the muzzle of the wolf.

The reaction was even more extreme than he could have hoped for. The creature sprang away from him and cowered on the ground, rubbing violently at its eyes and nostrils with its paws and whimpering pathetically.

Martin was barely able to stand, but he could see his sword, just out of reach. He bent, picked it up and swung all in one motion. The follow-through made him stagger and almost fall, but the stroke cleaved the wolf's head in two.

And then he did fall, in a dead faint, over the wolf's still twitching body. The last thing he heard was the howls of the pack as they approached.

CHAPTER 5

28th OCTOBER, 1745 SOUTH EAST OF CARLISLE

Sean woke with a start.

"Martin?" he said beneath his breath, but there was no reply, although he was convinced his friend had called out to him.

He stood, stiff from a night spent lying on the ground, and began to stretch. The bones in his back creaked and snapped, and a chill seemed to have settled there that he knew from experience would take half a day to go away. The girl was still lying on the ground below him, eyes still staring vacantly. Sean had to look away—once he stared back into those eyes he could find himself lost there, lost for a long time.

He looked away, and that was when he saw the movement in the grass in front of him. He reached for his dagger, aware that he had left his musket strapped to a saddlebag which was itself strapped to the pony.

He wasn't given time to get the dagger out of the sheath—a figure stood up in the grass and Sean was looking down the muzzle of a musket, just as there was a flash of red and he was hit high on the chest near his collar bone, knocking him over and down on top of the girl.

The blow hit him hard, as if someone had taken a hammer to his whole left-hand side, but he was still conscious. The pain, although severe, was not enough to stop him moving. As he heard more brigands arriving, heavy footsteps tramping through the grass, he slipped his dagger from its sheath and held it fast in his right hand, hidden beneath his body.

"I got him. I got him. Shot him right in the head. Did you see, Father? Did you see?"

It sounded like a child, but Sean did not want to lift his head to find out—he wanted them to think he was down for good. He tried to still his breathing and relax his body, but the pain from his wound was making him tremble and shake all over.

"Aye, you got him all right, but I don't think it was in the head," a deeper voice said. "Just don't get too close just yet—I'm not sure that gun of yours could bring down a dog, never mind a full grown man."

And in truth, Sean had been wondering the same thing. Oh, it hurt all right—it hurt like hell— but there was no grating of smashed bone, and seemingly no huge exit wound. If he had been hit at that range by a normal musket he would not now be breathing, never mind thinking of a counter attack. He hoped that the brigands would be too keen for plunder to notice how little damage the shot had done.

"Father," came another voice from slightly further off. "Can I have the woman first this time? Can I?"

So, this wasn't a one off. His attackers were seasoned brigands. That was going to make his job harder—opportune thieves were more likely to be frightened off by a spirited opponent, but seasoned campaigners, like these seemed to be, would be ready for anything. Beneath his body his hand started to tremble as he heard the footsteps in the grass getting ever closer.

"Come, Father," the voice said, and there was a thin whining quality to it that Sean recognised with embarrassment from his own youth. "You had the last two, and they died before we could get to them. You said. You did. You—"

There was a sound as of flesh on flesh, and Sean realised that the father had hit one of the boys, and hard by the sound of it. He might not get a better chance.

He rolled off the girl beneath him and got to his feet as quickly as he was able. The world swam about him, and a white-hot pain lanced through his whole upper body, but he found he was staring at the exposed back of the adult attacker. He stabbed, hard, aiming for the kidneys. The knife went in its full length before Sean pulled it out again. If Martin had been there to see the look of triumph, he would have recognised little of his friend. The man stood up straight, hands clutching at his wound, back arched, head up, and Sean caught him in a neck lock with his left arm, a move that caused the world to go black around Sean but left him enough consciousness to pull the knife across the man's throat, hard, bringing a hot gush of blood over both of them. The man's body went limp in his arms and he let it fall to the ground at his feet. There was a wet, gurgling sound, but it only lasted a few seconds, then there was only a corpse left behind.

He had just dropped the man when something jumped on his back, legs wrapped around his waist, arms pummeling around his head, a screaming devil that he was unable to dislodge. He tried to get his dagger around, making short stabbing motions over his head that finally brought a sharp squeal of pain, but this was rewarded by two small thumbs finally finding his eyes and beginning to press, hard. Sean threw himself backwards, his whole body weight coming down on his attacker. He heard bones snap, but didn't have time to wonder if they were his own, for the third attacker was on him, a thin knife darting and flickering. Sean rolled off the still body of the second assailant and faced the new threat.

"You've killed my father!" the figure in front of him said, and Sean realised with a jolt that it was only a boy, a youth no more than twelve years old who barely came up to Sean's chest. His clothes were ragged and torn, and he looked like he had not eaten for a week—no, make that several weeks. His hair hung forward across his face in lank ropy strands, and it was caked with such mud that it was impossible to tell its colour. Open sores ran across the boy's cheeks, red and weeping, and there was a wheezing throatiness in his voice that spoke of the wasted lungs inside.

"Put down your weapon," Sean said. "I wish you no harm."

The boy laughed.

"That's fuckin' rich. Look what you've done to my father, you've slit his bloody throat— where's the harm in that?" he said, gesticulating with the knife at the bloody figure on the ground. And then the boy noticed the other figure, lying still beside his father.

"Tom?" he said, and now there was a sob in his voice. "Wake up Tom—we've got to kill us this bastard."

He never took his eyes off Sean as he moved round to check on the smaller figure. As soon as Sean saw him raise the head and saw the way it flopped back down, he knew that Tom would not be waking up anytime soon—the boy's neck was broken. He felt a sudden burst of sorrow, and rage at a father who could lead his sons to death, but he fought off all emotion—he had an armed opponent to face, and his training told him that calm was required here, not hot blood.

The remaining brigand howled, a noise unique in Sean's experience, the pain and sorrow in it almost too much to bear.

"Look. Take your dead and leave. There has been enough blood shed here." Sean said, dismayed to hear the tremor that pain and fatigue had brought to his voice, "I bear you no more malice."

"Oh, you bear me no malice? Is that it? You kill my father, and my ten-year-old brother. Aye, that's right, ten years old. And I get to walk away?"

He spat on the ground at Sean's feet. "I'll see the colour of your guts first. And then I'll pish on your bones."

The knife came up fast, so that Sean had to take a step backwards, and even then he felt the air part in its passing. He still held his own dagger, but was loathed to use it.

"I didn't mean to kill your brother," he said, realising that he meant it—he should have found a different way. "Look. I've got meat in my saddlebags, and some silver I can let you have. Just put down the knife. I'm bigger than you, and fitter, and I'm trained in knife fighting—I wouldn't want to kill you too."

Sean saw doubt in the boy's eyes, and the dagger lowered, only fractionally, yet it lowered. Sean was beginning to believe that he might get out of this without another fight when he caught a movement over the boy's shoulder, and looked up to see Mary, standing beside the pony, Sean's musket raised and pointing at his attacker. The eyes still stared vacantly, but now they were staring at a spot near the top of the young brigand's head.

"No!" Sean shouted, and the boy turned to follow his shout. The musket went off, the boy taking it full on, a blast which shredded and dissolved his face and scalp into ribbons of flesh and blew most of the top of his head off before he fell like a stone over the body of his father.

Sean bent forward and threw up violently in the grass by his feet.

When he was finally able to stand upright, feeling as weak as if he had just spent a week in a sick bed, he saw that Mary was still standing by the pony, still with the musket raised to her shoulder. He walked over and gently took the gun from her. She allowed herself to be led to one side, away from the bodies that were already attracting flies. Her eyes stared into the distance, and there was no sign of any memory of what she had just done.

Sean had no time for reflection. He examined his shoulder and was surprised to find only a small wound, a homemade pellet embedded just under the skin. Fortifying himself with some wine from the saddlebags, he dug the pellet out—a rough, quarter-inch slug of metal. He had been lucky—the boy's aim had obviously been off and he had caught the edge of the spread of pellets. He didn't like to look at the boy Mary had shot—it reminded him of how close he had been to looking the same.

The pain was huge as the pellet came out, but after washing and binding the wound there was only a dull ache there. His shirt was ruined, covered in mud and blood and torn so much that he used the clean bits that remained to clean himself up. Afterwards he balled it up and tossed it into the undergrowth, leaving his arms bare under a leather waistcoat.

Now came the part he was dreading. He had to get the bodies out of sight before anyone came along. He couldn't afford to be involved in any investigation, even if he had been in the right.

The children were the worst. They felt light, and he guessed that they weighed no more than five stone each. Their bodies were covered in bruises, both old and new, along with boils and sores in such profusion that the skin was completely obscured in places. The smaller child's head lolled on the end of the body as if badly attached, and Sean's stomach turned at the thought that he was responsible for the death of one so young.

He found a spot between two thick bushes of gorse and laid the bodies in a small natural hollow before returning for the father.

Sean's knife cut had opened the throat completely, almost severing the head. The body was lying in a pool of blood that had already attracted a swarm of large blue flies. They rose sluggishly in the air and buzzed around Sean's head as he dragged the body, feet first, to lie with the others. Once all three were under the bushes, he pulled more undergrowth over them to ensure they would not be seen easily. There was nothing he could do about the blood on the grass, but the first rain would deal with that. He wished that he had time to give them a decent burial, especially the children, but he knew that he had to get out of this area as quickly as possible, and hope that no one apart from the brigands had noticed their passing.

After he hid the bodies, he had to stop and rest. There were black spots floating in front of his eyes and his wound throbbed constantly. He drank some more wine from his rapidly diminishing ration and ate some dry bread and cheese. He tried to get Mary to eat with him, but her lips remained tightly shut. He told himself that she would eat when she was hungry, that she would have to, but deep down he believed that she did not eat—that whatever sickened in her also in some way sustained her.

He ate fast, rolling up their bedding between mouthfuls, and in five minutes he was getting Mary up on to the pony and heading off down the narrow path they had been following.

They had travelled on little used tracks since leaving Milecastle, nearly thirty hours earlier. Old Menzies had laid out the general direction for him, and put him on this current trail, but Sean was already well past the limit of his knowledge of the area—that had been passed yesterday afternoon when they skirted Carlisle.

Sean remembered the bustle he had seen in the town. The Thane's messengers had made better time than he, and taken easier roads, and the town was full of rumours of war—barricades were being built, garlic was being spread, and there was a steady stream of townspeople leaving, taking the main road south to safety.

But Sean was not on the main road. He had given the town a wide berth and had watched the exodus from some three miles away. Not that he could have taken the main road anyway—those townspeople would have slaughtered a bitten one on first sight, even one as beautiful as Campbell's daughter. Sean had kept them out of sight of the exodus by travelling in ditches and behind hedgerows, but even then it had been impossible to escape the crowds of people. He had to hide in a thick copse of hawthorn for the best part of the afternoon as cart after cart made its slow way along the road, and by the time the passing escapees thinned to a trickle, it was almost dark again. In the gathering gloom Sean had led them as far from the main road as he dared, but it had meant a long detour for them, and when darkness finally fell he was unsure of his bearings and had to stop.

He had dreamed during the night, of dark shadows that were too fast to kill, shadows who took Mary Campbell from him. In the dream he chased her down dark tunnels, mile after mile, her white form ever evading his futile grasp. And it all took place in a dead, echoing blackness where there was no sound.

In the dark hours before dawn, he had woken to find her staring at the sky, heavy tears misting her eyes. He embraced her, holding her close, but she did not move to return the hug. She kept staring at the sky, and after a while the tears stopped, and Sean lay there beside her, weaving fantasies of wife and home and child. Her thoughts remained her own, locked behind the stare that was the last thing he saw before sleep took him again, but it was fitful at best, and he was still unsure as to whether he had really heard the voice of Martin, his friend. Then the brigands had come.

He put it to the back of his mind—the day was getting on, and Sean reckoned they had lost nearly a day's travelling time already due to the previous day's detours. He upped the speed to a brisk walk. Before long they hit a steep path which rose steadily into the hills around the lakes. At first cloud and mist hung over them, and Sean was grateful for it obscuring their passage, but the relentless drizzle left him damp and uncomfortable, and he was glad when the sun finally appeared in the late afternoon.

Sean was still trembling in the aftermath of the fight, and the sight of the head lolling on the broken neck kept pushing itself forward in his mind. He had never killed before, and although he had been trained as an officer of the watch, it was one thing to hack with a sword at bags of straw, or to shoot at a wooden effigy, but quite another to feel a hot body go heavy and limp in your hands. He twitched at the slightest movement around him and once very nearly fired his musket at a blackbird rustling in a hedgerow, but as the sun warmed him and the chill slowly faded, he found himself, more and more, stealing glances at the girl on the pony.

She still had not spoken, and, apart from the killing of the brigand, had not moved of her own volition. She just sat there, moving in time with the pony, staring straight ahead down the road. He wondered what had compelled her to shoot the brigand. It was obvious that a dangerous situation had brought her back from whatever depths she dreamt in, but she had returned just as quickly to her waking sleep. In the light of day, her eyes were clear, but still they stared blankly into the distance, as if wondering what the future might hold.

He still did not really comprehend why he was so attracted to her. He had known more beautiful women, and certainly more accessible ones, but there had never before been one who beguiled him so completely that he felt like a clumsy youth in her presence. Maybe it was for the best that she did not speak—he had no idea how he would begin to talk to her.

By mid-afternoon the road brought them to the side of a small lake, and Sean drew the pony to a halt. This was as good a place as any for them to eat and rest, and for him to wipe the muck of battle from his body and his mind. They were now making good time—by Sean's reckoning, they had travelled nearly sixty miles since leaving Milecastle, about forty of them in the direction he was meant to be taking. He was beginning to feel it in his legs, though, and, not for the first time, he wished for a pony of his own.

He lifted Mary down off the pony. Did her arm tighten around his shoulders as he did it? He wasn't sure, and when he looked in her eyes there was only the blank stare. But maybe she was coming out of it—whatever it was. He put it to the back of his mind. There were more pressing concerns.

Old Menzies had packed the saddlebags for their journey, and while Sean was thankful for wine, bread and cheese, he wished that the old man lived on a more varied diet. He decided to risk leaving Mary alone for a few minutes while he foraged—and bathed. He was not surprised that the girl took no notice of him—he smelt worse than a ram on a wet day.

He walked, fully clothed, into the lake and splashed around, making sure all the blood and mud was washed from his arms, his clothes and his hair, and kept washing until the water stopped running pink, then walked out of the lake to look for food.

When he returned to their camp ten minutes later, he was carrying a trout, some apples and some blackberries, but as he approached the spot where he'd left the pony, he realised his trip was in vain—for Mary's sake, anyway. She had raided the saddlebags and was eating—no, not eating, devouring—a large chunk of cheese. But her mouth moved mechanically, and crumbled bits fell unattended in her lap.

Sean tried to get her to eat some blackberries, but he merely smeared the juices of them around her mouth, and the sight of the redness there, so much like blood, made him stop. He cleaned her up as best as he was able, and she sat in the shade of the tree, still staring straight ahead, while he prepared a fire and cooked the fish.

Nothing moved over the loch, and even the clouds seemed fixed in the sky overhead. Only the merest ripple disturbed the water, and Sean believed he could be at rest here, so far from the chains of duty that bound him to the wall. He sat with his back to a tree and surveyed the scene while his clothes dried on his body.

He had wished often enough for some change to come, some end to the routine, and now he had it, along with the care of a beautiful woman and a journey to parts unknown. He threw back his head and laughed, disturbing a heron on the shore into flight, then suddenly was solemn.

That had been stupid, even here where they seemed to be the only people for miles. More care was needed, and fast travel. He had no idea how he would approach old Menzies' friend, or even if he could actually find the man, but he had made his vow to Campbell, and he intended to follow it through as much as he was able. And if it came to fighting, well, he was well-trained, and they'd have to kill him before he would give up the girl.

Before setting off again he checked his shoulder, but the wound was clean. There was little blood, and only a dull pain, not unlike toothache. He bound it up again. If Menzies' friend was such a good doctor, maybe he'd let the man take a look at it. But first they had to reach him.

For the rest of the day they travelled along a high ridge, looking down into empty valleys and lakes shining blue in the sun. There was little sign of human influence here apart from the dry stone walls that spoke of long ago endeavour. Buzzards circled high overhead, and occasionally they would flush a deer out of the undergrowth, but apart from that it was as if they had the landscape to themselves. Sean slowly forgot about the killings that morning. He had expected trouble on the road, and he had found it and dealt with it. Now he had to look forward, not back. But he knew that the sight of the boy's head lolling on a broken neck would haunt his dreams for a long time to come.

As the sun began to descend into the western hills, they came to the last hill on the ridge, and Sean found himself looking out over what seemed to be an endless plain, a plain which, even as he watched, was being lit by red points of light, clusters of towns preparing for the night to come. His heart sank—surely there weren't that many people in the world, that many people between him and his goal? But then no one had told him it was going to an easy journey.

He began to search for a place to stop for the night—he needed to do some thinking, to find a way to get Mary across that plain without her sickness being discovered.

He found what he was looking for half an hour later—a secluded knoll within a valley, with a small stream gurgling past them and a flat spot to sleep on. He fed and watered the pony before turning back to Mary.

It was nearly full dark by now, and the stars were winking into being overhead. Mary was standing where he had left her, but her face was raised up, her eyes staring skywards, her head cocked to one side, as if listening to someone.

"Mary?" he said, but got no response. He reached out to touch her arm, and she moved, as fast as a cat, to push him way. Even as he stood back, astonished, she began to walk, northwards, back along the path they had recently descended.

"Hey!" he shouted. "Where are you going?" He ran after her and grabbed her by the left arm, but she swung round, her right hand flexed like a claw, and he was just able to pull back in time as the talons of her fingernails passed in front of his eyes. And as quickly as she had reacted, she turned back to the road again and kept walking. In the quick glimpse he got as she attacked him, Sean had seen that her eyes still stared blankly ahead, not even registering his presence.

He ran after her, passed her and stood in the centre of the path. She showed no signs of stopping, or even recognising that he was there. She was like an automaton he had once seen Menzies play with, a grotesque parody of a person, moving only by the whim of another. He braced himself and swung a punch that connected squarely with her jaw and sent her, insensible, to the ground.

Immediately he knelt beside her, checking that she was still breathing. She was, and he said a small prayer, but her eyes were now closed, and a heavy bruise was already darkening her chin.

He managed to carry her back to their camp, and he laid her down gently on the ground. Her complete stillness, even an apparent lack of life itself, gave him an idea for the morrow, but in the meantime he sat and watched over her, afraid to take his eyes off her as the stars wheeled overhead and the night passed.

Sometime later he did sleep, sitting cross-legged on the ground beside the prone body. His head drooped slowly and hung on his chest, so he didn't see the girl's eyes open, nor the tears which once more hung in the corners before rolling down her cheeks. But she did not move, merely stared at the sky, her eyes filled with the reflections of stars.

Sean woke with a start in the morning, suddenly afraid that while he slept, his ward might have gone wandering once more, but she was still lying on the ground beside him, her eyes open but unseeing.

He remembered his thought of the night before, and unwrapped the large cloaks they were both using as bedding. He laid Mary down on one of these, then rolled her up into both until she was cocooned. He made sure that there was a passageway to allow air in, then carried her to the pony and laid her face down, sideways across its back. She did not move or make a sound of complaint. She was going to have an uncomfortable journey, that was for sure, but it was preferable to having her out on show where she might be murdered by the first person to realise she was bitten.

He intended to pass her off as a corpse—a country girl being returned for burial to her hometown. It was flimsy, and not very believable, but it was all he could think of right now. All he needed to do was get his story right, and believe it himself as much as he was able.

He had plenty of time to think on it. The path down from the hills to the plain was narrow, steep and treacherous, and he had to lead the pony slowly through some bad spots so that it was gone mid-day before he put the hills behind him. And in all that time there had not been a noise, nor a movement from the bundle on the back of the pony.

In the first town he passed through—little more than a

hamlet with a blacksmith and an inn— nobody paid any attention to him. Nor did they in the second, a staggered collection of weavers' cottages strung out along a low hill. But the further south he went, the bigger the towns became and the more outlandish his dress appeared among the clean, fine clothed, denizens. His luck held throughout that day, though—no one approached him, and he in turn spoke to no one.

It was like being in a different world. The countryside through which they passed was managed and manicured, with farms and homesteads dotted across it like a rash. The road on which he travelled was crisscrossed with trails and rutted pathways, even occasionally another road, and several times he had to make decisions at crossroads with no signposts. All he knew was that he was still heading south.

Dusk was falling before they met anyone travelling in the other direction. A youth, about the same age as the one Sean had killed, led a huge shire horse along the road. But this was no sickly child. The boy radiated good health, his freckled face breaking into a huge smile as he saw Sean.

"Well met, fellow," the youth said. "I thought I was the only person on the road. Will you tarry and break bread with me?"

He must have seen by Sean's face that he was not keen to stop.

"I have ale," the boy said, and that was enough for Sean.

They sat under the shade of a large tree. Sean shared some bread and cheese, and drank gratefully of the boy's ale. The beer was thinner, less strong than he was accustomed to, but it was all the better—it would not cloud his head.

He told the boy the news from the north, but the lad scoffed at him.

"Oh, aye. The Boy King again, is it. According to my grandfather he has been coming every year for the past fifty."

Sean thought of unrolling Mary Campbell from the rug, just to shake the boy out of his complacency, but his good sense got the better of him, and when the boy asked about the package, the lie about the dead serving girl passed easily from his lips.

The boy took the story without a question, merely muttering a silent prayer to himself at the mention of death, and when they parted, Sean's heart had lifted somewhat and he felt more confident in his ability to pass through this area.

Nightfall found them between towns, and he managed to find a quiet spot by a river, making sure that they were alone before finally unrolling Mary from the blankets.

He had left her alone there all day, and there had been no sign of life the whole time. He told himself that she had shown no sign of needing food or water, but he still felt more like a jailer than a protector as he unwrapped her.

He had to check, twice, to make sure she was still breathing, and he had a bad moment when he was sure she had died on him, but then those eyes which so bewitched him snapped open, and she stared past him at the sky once more.

She still would not eat, not taking anything he offered, merely sitting in silence while he ate the last of the cheese and bread and finished the last of the wine. They were now out of food.

All that remained were some apples from the day before. Tomorrow he would have to purchase some rations, but he would think of that in the morning. For now, he had another night of watching and waiting ahead of him.

He had considered not stopping—walking through the night with the girl still rolled up on the pony was one way to ensure she did not wander, but fatigue told him that he needed a rest, and common sense told him that anyone travelling at night was bound to raise even more suspicion. He had little idea how far they had come, nor how far they had to go, but Menzies had reckoned on anything up to five days, so he had a deal of walking yet to do.

While he was eating, the sun had set fully and darkness had fallen over them. He dared not light a fire and, with cloud cover overhead, he could barely see the pale face of the girl although she was only a few feet away from him.

He unrolled the bedding, laid her down, and settled down to wait. A light drizzle started to fall, and he was soon damp through, the cold water running down his back under his waistcoat, but he sat still. He didn't have long to wait.

She sat bolt upright, her head cocked to one side in a gesture he remembered from the night before. Then she tried to stand, but he laid his body over hers and pinned her to the ground with his weight. She struggled underneath him, and he felt the wound tear open at his shoulder, but she didn't have the weight to push him off. A few minutes later she went limp, and the blank stare was back in her eyes. She mouthed some words, as if talking to someone, but there was no sound, and she was quiet once more. Sean stayed where he was, and in that way they lay together all night, him getting a fitful sleep, she staring skywards, the rain falling into her eyes and mingling with the tears that lay there.

Once more he dreamed. She ran from him, down dark corridors, always just ahead of him until the corridor opened out. Not into a chamber, no, but because this was a dream, it opened out into a large open area of rough ground. And still she ran from him.

She turned, and there was a laughing smile in her eyes. But there was no humour there, only a mocking leer.

"Run as hard as you can, my child," she said, but it was a man's voice that came from her. "But you will never catch her. She is mine, and she always will be."

Sean woke with a start, a cold sweat running over his body. He slept no more that night.

The next day dawned cold, damp and misty. Sean repeated his actions of the day before, rolling the girl up in the bedding and settling her on the pony before setting out on the road once more. Within an hour they had passed through another small village, and Sean looked for any sign of a trader who would sell him some food, but the hour was too early and no one had yet stirred. He did see his first signpost, though, and it informed him that he was within five miles of Garstang. That in itself meant nothing to him, but if a town was big enough to merit a signpost, it would be big enough to have traders who could sell him some food.

A little over an hour later, he arrived at the outskirts of

the town, and the foot traffic on the road increased considerably. Sean found himself walking close to the pony—as close to be almost touching it, but if anyone was intrigued by his presence, or the bundle on the back of the pony, no one spoke of it.

He found out why ten minutes later. It was market day in town, and people were coming in from far and wide, many with ponies, and many with strangely shaped bundles. He felt slightly less conspicuous as he approached the town centre in the middle of a small group of travellers, all grumbling about the state of the weather. If there had been any news of the Boy King's return, it certainly hadn't reached here yet—all the talk was of commerce, and how much trade could be expected that day.

The town was built around a market square, with coaching inns on either side, and the area between them was teeming with people setting up stall or laying out their wares on the ground. No one was paying attention to Sean.

The sights and sounds of the market overwhelmed him. Nothing in his life in Milecastle had prepared him for the riot of colours, noises and smells around him. Back at the wall, market day meant that the farmers brought their produce in to the town for selling and trade. And that was all.

But here there was trade of all kinds, in spices and cloth from faraway lands, in wines and liquor, scent and perfumes that left a heady aroma in the air. There were weapons and armour, still shiny and clean, and fine leather jerkins, boots and belts.

And the people! Sean was beginning to realise how much his people were quelled by the presence of the wall. Here there was no such inhibition.

Gentlemen and ladies both wore fine clothing, and even the children were clean and fully covered. At every turn there as some new sight to see. But as well as new surprises, there was much that appalled him.

Wherever he went he was accosted by hawkers and beggars. Many had limbs missing, or their bodies were hideously disfigured. Dead cats and dogs lay in the gutters, and rats ran openly among the discarded rubbish at the sides of the market square. Women raised their skirts for passers-by, proving that they were clean by showing their private parts. Several of them made obscene gestures in Sean's direction and laughed when he blushed and turned away.

But still there was much to amaze him. There were jugglers, knife throwers, fire-eaters, contortionists and strongmen. Sean was almost tempted by an offer to wrestle "The Moor" for a shilling as, although the man was huge, he looked slow and clumsy, but he couldn't afford to leave the side of the pony.

He had been wandering for five minutes before he remembered that he was supposed to be looking for food. But during that short time the crowd had grown by such an extent that he was penned in on all sides by bodies.

Luckily for him the crowd around him was suddenly distracted by a loud shout from across the square.

"See the hog-faced lady," the voice said.

"Watch her eat from her trough."

"A farthing for anyone who will kiss her."

The crowd moved away from around Sean. By standing in the stirrups to gain some extra height, he could see over their heads.

They were crowded around a heavily built figure wearing a long, expensively cut, dress.

"All the way from Bavaria," the caller shouted above the noise of the crowd. "See the hog- faced lady."

The caller had been right—it did seem to have a pig's face. But it was no lady. If Sean wasn't mistaken, they were queuing up to kiss a shaved bear, one drugged enough to keep it docile, then dressed in a lady's finery.

Sean had only ever seen one bear in his life, and that had been a poor wasted specimen that danced to fiddle music and didn't have the spirit to try and break its chains. He half-hoped that this one had some of its wild nature left—it would be a fine thing to see this throng in the face of a fully awake bear.

The crowd had cleared around him as they crushed

forward to see the "lady". Now was as good a time as any to purchase the provisions he would need—he could see everything he could want laid out around him.

There were loaves of bread, as long as his arm and still steaming from the ovens, there was meat in such quantity that would feed a small army, and there were more varieties of fish than Sean knew existed in the world. People were shouting from all sides, clamouring for attention and their share of the trade. Sean could not see much point in it all—there seemed to be few people now around apart from other traders. Surely all they were doing was moving their goods around, shuffling their packages into new configurations, then going away convinced they'd had a good days trade? It was something he would never understand—but then old Menzies had told him years ago when he was but a boy that Sean wasn't cut out for a life in trade.

The first stall holder, where he bought bread, hardly even looked at him, but the meat stall- holder he decided on proved to be much more garrulous—disastrously so.

"So, down for the market, are we?" the small fat man said. Sean grunted a response, hoping that would suffice, but the man wasn't to be put off. "What are you selling, then? By the size of that bundle it looks like a good size carcass in there."

The man moved close to the pony, and Sean had to be quick to cut him off. Although the man was small and rotund, he was surprisingly nimble on his feet.

"I'm not selling anything—just passing through. I didn't even know that today was market day," Sean said. He tried to get his body between the fat man and the bundle. But he wasn't quick enough.

"Nonsense," the butcher said. "Everyone is selling something. I'll tell you what, if it's venison, I'll take it off your hands, no questions asked." He dropped a slow wink and tapped the side of his nose. "What the Protector can't see can't hurt him."

And at that he slapped hard on the bundle of bedding. Sean winced, but there was no noise from within.

"Nice firm flesh too by the look of things," the trader

said. "Come now, name your price."

Sean pushed the fat man away from the body. In his haste to get the man away from the bundle he pushed slightly too hard, and the fat man staggered, almost losing his footing.

"I have told you: I have nothing for sale."

He saw, too late, that he had made the man suspicious.

"Look," he said, lowering his voice and pretending to bring the trader in on a secret. "I've got a body on the back of the pony—a young girl from Carlisle who died in childbirth. Her father in Sheffield is paying me to take her back for burial, but there was a bit of a scandal—no one could find the child's father—so I'm doing this the quiet way. To avoid any unpleasantness."

The stall-holder was suddenly full of bluster.

"If you don't want to sell to me, then just say so. Don't try and hoodwink me with a tall yarn. A body on the back of a pony like that—in the middle of the market—it's preposterous."

The man want back towards his stall, muttering under his breath, all bluster and blow, and it was all Sean could do to stop himself laughing. He was brought back to earth with a bump by a voice from behind him.

"What's this about a body?"

Sean turned, and found himself faced with one of the largest men he had ever seen, and his heart sank when he saw the red tunic of a Warden of the Law. The man was bigger even than Constable Barnstable, and he towered over Sean by at least four inches. His booted feet looked capable of doing severe damage to a body, and his hands looked big enough to crush a person's skull. He reminded Sean of one of the great brown bears that were sometimes seen on the north side of the wall, but this man looked even more formidable—there was an intelligence in his eyes that no bear could achieve.

"A body, sir? I heard no mention of any such thing."

But by now the fat trader had turned back.

"Aye, he says he has a body in yon bundle, but I'm betting it's a haunch of venison. Go on, ask him what he's doing here."

Sean shot the butcher a glance that would have cowed anyone less sure of himself. The butcher merely stared back, a thin smile rising at the corners of his mouth. Sean could almost see his thoughts—he was hoping yet to get a cheap haunch of venison.

"You know that poaching venison is illegal?" the big man asked Sean, and there was a sudden stillness about the man that Sean recognised. He saw a readiness for fight or flight that he had seen many times in his opponents on the training grounds. He decided it would not be wise to cross this man—he only hoped he had enough wit to get himself out of the situation.

"I promise you, sir, the trader is mistaken. I have no venison," he said. He pulled at the pony's reins, getting the animal's attention away from some loose straw on the road. "I'll be moving on now—I have a long way to travel."

A hand reached out and pulled his shoulder. He almost cried out as his wound flared once more.

"I believe I had better have a look anyway," the officer said, and pushed Sean to one side, heading for the bundle. Sean knew that once the thing was unrolled he had no chance of escape. He reached for his sword just as the officer put his hand inside the rolls of cloth.

He saw the look of surprise which crossed the officer's face—the man hadn't seen him as a threat until now. Sean thought he might have a chance if he took advantage of the situation quickly, But he had only got the top inch of his sword free from the scabbard when he caught a movement to his left as the fat trader swung something in the air, and he had time only to shift his head slightly sideways before it hit him from behind and sent him away into darkness.

He came to slowly. The room he was in was dim, and it took him some seconds to realise that the reason for the dimness was that night was falling. Through a small, barred, window he was able to watch the colour leeching from the sky—he had been out for the best part of the daylight hours.

He was in a cell, an eight-foot by eight-foot cube with an

iron grating for a door. He was lying on a stone bench, cold leeching into his back. It took him long minutes before he was able to focus properly, and when he tried to sit up it felt like someone was drilling a hole in the back of his head.

He felt under his hair. He had a lump the size of a duck's egg, but his hand came away dry— there was no blood. He tried to stand and the room swam around him, but he able to stagger as far as the door and grab hold of the cold iron bars.

"I need to speak to someone," he shouted. "It's important."

At first there was no reply, but there was a noise from a room beyond as if someone was moving about, so Sean shouted again, louder this time.

"I need to speak to the Warden. Lives may depend on it."

There was a grumbling from the room beyond, then the huge figure of the Warden filled the corridor beyond Sean's bars.

"In Jesu's name boy—you can even cause trouble in an empty room. At least it proves to me that you're alive though—I've never seen anyone felled with a leg of lamb before and I wasn't sure what to expect."

"What time is it?" Sean asked, interrupting him.

"Dusk. You've been here the best part of six hours. The doctor said you would wake up eventually, but I wasn't so sure."

"And the girl? What of the girl?" Sean asked, trying, but not succeeding, to keep the panic out of his voice."

"Your wife, is she?" the big man asked. "Or someone else's?" He made a lascivious gesture with a hand at his groin. "I might even have kept her rolled up in a blanket myself, just to keep other men away from her."

Sean growled in growing frustration. The Warden took his time before replying, as if considering his words carefully.

"Oh, she's well enough. No, that's the wrong word. I have rarely seen anyone less well. But she's not dead, put it that way."

Sean let out a long low sigh.

"I told you I had no venison."

"That you did, young sir. And fair vexed the butcher was as well. Although you damned near caused a riot in the market. When I unrolled that bundle, and she fell out onto the road, the crowd there wanted to hang you on the spot. And I might have let them, if that little fat butcher hadn't noticed she was breathing. The doctor is with her now."

Sean's panic grew.

"You must watch her. She is ill, and at night she...she wanders if she is not secured."

"Aye, we'll watch her close enough. But we will be watching you closer." The Warden scratched his massive belly. "Although I don't see as we can charge you with anything at the moment—not until she sees fit to speak."

"She won't be speaking—she has not said a word these past three months." Sean said.

He was aware he was in a tight spot. He had to find a way out of this cell. There was no telling what might happen to Mary Campbell when the doctor discovered she had been bitten.

"The doctor said that she seemed to have suffered some deep shock," the Warden said. "But if it was three months ago, why has she got a new bruise on her face? Surely it cannot have anything to do with that shot wound in your shoulder? And that is a far north accent you have there, boy. There are strange stories coming down from those parts, and I'll wager you have a strange one to tell of your own."

Sean considered telling the Warden the whole story, unburdening himself of the truth, but he could not afford the time. Already the sky was black outside the cell.

"Can I see her? We were to be married next spring, and she is more settled when she is with me."

The big Warden laughed, a deep booming thing that sent echoes round the cell.

"Settled? That would be as in 'battered and rolled up in bedding and laid over the back of a pony'. Aye, that'll be right. I can tell that you have concern for her, but I think I'll keep you two apart until such time as I know what is going on."

"Can a man and his wife not have a fight?" Sean said.

"Oh, I've seen many a lady after a man has put her in her place. But I don't think you are that kind of fellow. No. You must stay here until I have the truth of it."

Sean was about to remonstrate with the man when there was a commotion from the room beyond. A door banged loudly and a voice called for the Warden.

The big man looked at Sean.

"Not more of your doing, I hope?" But Sean shook his head

"How could it be? I've been out cold all day."

"That you have, young sir, but you have the air of someone who carries trouble around with him. I will be watching you closely."

He turned and left. Sean tested the strength of the iron bars, but there was no give in them. He hit the door hard in frustration.

There were raised voices in the room beyond. Sean couldn't make out any words, but he could tell that the Warden was angry with someone, and he was a man that Sean would not like to see angered.

Heavy footsteps crossed the room beyond, and once more the massive figure of the Warden appeared in the doorway. His face was flushed, and there was a cold fire in his eyes that made Sean glad there was a locked iron door between them.

"It seems you were right. Your lady has gone wandering. What you didn't tell me was that she is a murdering bitch. One of my men is dead, and the doctor here…" he said, motioning to a small man who came into view behind him. "He has almost had his eyes scratched out. And now I have to go out on a god forsaken night and find your lady, before she does any more damage."

"She is not herself," Sean said.

"I don't much care," the big man said. "She has left a widow and three fatherless children, and for that she will pay—whoever she may be."

The Warden handed the keys for the cells to the doctor.

"In case she gets me too. We wouldn't want our inmate to

starve to death. Not before we hang him anyway."

The big man stormed out of the room, and Sean felt the door slam as he left the building. He looked across the cell, seeing the doctor for the first time.

The man looked like he had been in a fight with a wildcat, and lost. Deep gouges ran the length of his face on both sides of his nose and, although they had been treated and cleaned, the runnels looked deep, red and very painful. He was a thin, almost frail man, with only a few stray strands of hair on his head and a small straggly beard right on the point of his chin. He looked like an ancient ram—the kind Sean had often put out of its misery when he was a herdsman. The doctor looked like he was in his own special kind of misery.

"Tell me what happened," Sean asked, and the old man sighed loudly before answering.

"Let me get some of Thomas's fine ale and a seat, and we'll tell stories into the night," he said. "I am likely to get little sleep this night anyway." He shuffled off to the next room.

To Sean's surprise, the old man returned with a pitcher and two mugs of ale, one of which he passed through the bars.

"Never drink alone. Rule one of living to a ripe old age," the doctor said, and drained half the mug before putting it down.

Sean took a sip from his to buy him time to think. He had to get out of here and find Mary before the Warden did, otherwise they could both be dead by morning. But first he needed to hear what had happened to the doctor, and to the Warden's man.

"That's a feisty girl you've got there," the doctor said, fingering his cuts and wincing at the pain his touch brought. "Although I fear she has marked me so that the ladies will not look me again."

He said it with such sincerity that Sean was forced to laugh.

The old man feigned mock outrage.

"You don't think I was a great ladies' man in my day? I'll

have you know I had my pick of the young women around here—although to tell you the truth there wasn't much choice."

He took a silver flask from his coat and poured a liberal measure from it into his ale.

"Brandy. Purely medicinal," the old man said and dropped a long slow wink.

Sean was getting impatient. "What happened? What did she do?"

And still the old man took his time, taking a long draw from his tankard before replying.

"They brought her to me this morning," he said, wiping foam from his lips. "I thought she was dead at first, but she was breathing perfectly normally. I tried to use the salts on her, but she didn't even blink. It was only when night fell that she turned into a hell cat."

"Come on, man," Sean said, almost shouting. "Tell me what happened."

The doctor took another sip from his flagon, and Sean had to stop himself from screaming in frustration.

"I was in the other room, trying to find a potion that might revive the lady, when I heard a scream from next door. I thought it was coming from her at first, so high and shrill it was, but when I entered the room, I found it was the guard the Warden had placed there."

The doctor stopped to drink more ale, finishing the mug and re-filling it to the brim from the pitcher.

"She had that guard by the balls, and she seemed intent on pulling his manhood out by the roots. He was squealing like a stuck pig, and the pair of them were staggering and falling about the room like alehouse drunkards. And then he tripped over a fallen chair, and she fell on him."

"She had his throat torn open with her teeth before I could even step into the room. And when she stood and turned towards the door, there was blood, at her mouth, and all down the front of her clothing, and her eyes stared through me as if I wasn't there."

He raised his ale mug and drained it in one gulping

motion. Sean would not like to get into a drinking competition with this one—he might be small but it looked like he had hollow legs.

"I tried to stop her. Not for long, though. You can see what size I am, and I'm not the man I once was. Once she had done this," he said, motioning at the scars on his face, "I let her go, then I came here. The rest you know."

"And did you tell the Warden which way she went?" Sean asked

"No. I could not. I did not see her leave—I was tending as well as I could to the poor fellow on the floor. But his wounds were too severe—he died in my arms."

Sean had a chance. The Warden could not know that she always seemed to wander in the same direction, always north. He was about to ask another question when the doctor spoke again.

"Of course, she won't get far. Not in her condition."

Sean asked what he meant, and after the doctor told him, he was silent for a long time.

"You are sure?" he asked, and the old man nodded over the top of his beer.

"You look pale, boy," the old man said. "Are you well?"

Given the opening, Sean didn't need another chance. He pretended to be in pain from his wound. As he knew he would, the doctor opened the cell gate to come in and it was a simple matter to overpower him. The old man didn't struggle. Once Sean took the keys off him he sat, quiet, on the bench. Sean left him the remainder of the ale, though. It seemed only fair.

He left the old man there, pouring the last draught from his silver flask into the beer, and headed for the guardroom beyond.

He was looking for a weapon, but he was to be disappointed. There was a thick ledger which had Sean listed as 'name and origin unknown', and apart from the furniture, the only other thing in the room was a long woolen coat.

It was obvious when he tried it on that it belonged to the doctor—he could barely get his hands into the sleeves, never mind his arms.

doctor in Sheffield. He could get another musket, but he was loathed to part with the sword—it was the only thing he had ever had of his father's, and he had resolved always to have it by him. But if it was a choice between that and Mary Campbell, there was only going to be one winner.

Ten minutes later, he was on the outskirts of the town headed north, his mind buzzing with the implication of what the doctor had told him.

He was no longer looking for just a girl. He was looking for a pregnant girl, pregnant with a child of the Others.

CHAPTER 6

2nd NOVEMBER, 1745 MILECASTLE

Martin dreamed.

The scenes came to him in strange tableaux, where he knew all the names, all their histories, the past that had led up to these moments. They flowed past him, and he was an observer only. Several times he cried out, in recognition, in fear, in horror, but there was no sound, and the tableaux spun on in a seemingly endless stream. The first then...

There is a man, but such a man as has never been seen before—the very air seems to quiver and tremble in his presence. He is thin, almost to the point of emaciation, but there is a life in his eyes, a life that burns with a red fury. It is a wonder he is not consumed from the inside, such is the fire. His skin is like fine white marble, with red throbbing veins running through it, and his hair is so fine it blows in the slightest movement of air.

He stands before a long table, at which twelve men are seated. They are all in light robes, and are heavily bearded. They sit huddled in groups of two or three together. Unlike the one standing, they have features beaten and wrinkled by the sun. There is something of the Levant in their features, and although Martin has rarely seen a person not born in the British Isles, he knows they are Jewish.

In contrast to the others, the one standing is clean shaven, his long hair framing his face, giving him an almost womanly aspect. Martin realises that he has seen these features before, in the Boy King in the ruins of Jedburgh Abbey. The resemblance is striking. While they are obviously not the same man, they could indeed pass for brothers.

But where the Boy King had power, this one obviously is the vessel for something even stronger. He stands with hands outstretched, palms upwards, as if entreating the others to join him. To Martin the scene seems strangely familiar, but the dream has hold of his memory and will not let him remember.

In front of the standing man sits a golden chalice. It is a huge bowl nearly a foot in diameter, cunningly wrought in fine gold. Strange glyphs run in patterns across its surface, glyphs that seem to form swirling patterns of movement as the man lifts it off the table.

"Drink this in remembrance of me," the man says, and slits his wrist with a single slice of a razor sharp fingernail. There is the sudden smell of copper in the air and the man's blood flows, red and hot, into the chalice.

The air in the room seems to hum, and the gold flares, bathing the occupants in a deep orange glow. The man's eyes burn red as his followers make their covenant, each drinking in turn.

And after they have drank from the chalice, they each in turn approach the white one and bend their necks, allowing him to feed from them.

"This is your birthright," he says, and Martin finally sees that which his mind has been blocking. A young girl lies sprawled naked on the floor, her body heavily pregnant, the belly bulging with life that sends ripples of movement across her skin. The pale man steps forward and lifts the girl onto the table, the motion seemingly causing him no effort despite his frailty.

"Eat this in remembrance of me," he says. The twelve move forward to surround the girl, blocking her from Martin's view.

And the feast begins.

Martin calls out in horror, unable to turn his eyes from the foul deeds being perpetrated on the innocent. A red mist fills his vision, like the fine spray of blood from a badly slaughtered boar.

And the scene shifts, to a wooded grove in moonlight. Silver leaves rustle in dry trees, and the ground is dusty underfoot.

The second then.

A woman speaks. She has once been slim, but now she is heavily pregnant, her belly swollen almost to the point of bursting. Martin realises with amazement that it is the same girl he has seen at the supper. She shows no visible signs of wounding, and she shows no signs of fear. They are standing alone under a full moon, her and the pale one, and they are embracing.

They move apart and stare down the hill at the city below. There is a small line of torches heading out from the city, coming towards them.

"The centurions come, my Lord, as you said they would, "the woman says.

The pale man speaks, and his voice is like fine silk being drawn over planed wood.

"Yes. It was foreseen. But worry not. What is to come has to happen."

"What would you have me do?" the woman says.

"You need do nothing, say nothing. You carry the bloodline, and through you it will continue. If the final sacrifice is needed, then I am ready, but look for me in three days' time—if all is well we will have begun the great work, and we will leave together. The blood of my fathers will spring forth anew in a new land, and one day the Romans will see the true strength of a king of the Jews."

He embraces her tightly, his hand caressing the smooth bulge of her belly.

"You carry the future. Protect him for me."

They embrace once more before he pushes the woman away.

"Now go, and send Judas to me."

And Martin calls out, in anger at the blasphemy, but his voice is not heard.

Another figure enters the scene, one Martin has seen at the blasphemous feast.

"Judas," the pale one says. "Are you ready to meet your destiny?"

"I am, my Lord," the bearded man says, but he looks

worried.

The pale one clasps the other and hugs him tight to him.

"Our people will revile you, but I will always honour your name. Do this for me and you will sit at my right hand in times to come."

The bearded man nods, tears in his eyes, and moves away to meet the centurions who are just entering the clearing.

"That is him," he says, pointing at the pale one. "There is the one who calls himself the Son of God and the descendant of the giant-killer."

The centurions surround the pale one as the red mist descends once more. And through the mist, he hears the noise of stone being moved against stone, and the harsh panting of men exerting themselves.

The third then.

He is in the ruins of a once great building and Martin knows they are in a cave far underground.

Bearded men in white robes are digging among the fallen stones. At first Martin takes them for the twelve he has already seen, but these are not the tough weathered faces of hot climes; these are the white faces of Northerners.

They are digging by the light of huge lanterns set in the roof, the shifting of the air sending shadows swinging violently across the walls. The sides of the cave are rough stone in which are carved characters of great antiquity. And Martin knows that, although he doesn't understand the meaning, his woodsman friend would recognise these characters immediately.

The robed men look to have been digging for some time, dirt and mud ingrained in their clothing, their hair and their nails, and they are near the edge of exhaustion. Mounds of broken stone and dirt are strewn around the cave, evidence of places where digging has already taken place.

The dream continues, and the men keep digging. And Martin is beginning to wonder why he is being shown this when one of them lets out a cry of triumph and turns to their leader, an object wrapped in a drape of red velvet held reverentially in his hands.

Their leader is a tall man, lean and imperial in bearing. His long beard hangs low on his chest, his armour shining gold in the reflected light from the lanterns. Martin has seen this armoured man before, but the dream will not allow him to remember as the package is handed into the knight's hands and he unwraps it. Martin knows before he sees the gleam of the gold that the chalice is inside.

The man's eyes sparkle as he speaks.

"Baphomet told us true. Now the great work can begin anew and the Bloodline can be reclaimed."

"Praise the King," the diggers chant.

"His name will be exalted on high," the knight says, and is the first to slit his wrist and let the blood pour into the chalice.

The red mist descends again. And the scene shifts, heat turning to cold, the cave roof turning to a black sky outside a circle of stones.

The fourth then, and the last before awakening.

The stones jut proudly against the sky. Their surfaces gleam silver in the streaming moonlight. In the midst of the stones there is a female figure on the altar, and Martin cries out in recognition as he sees Mary Campbell laid out there, the black hair hanging down across the stone and the blue eyes staring at the sky. Around the stones, just outside the perimeter, twelve figures stand, silent and unmoving, mere shadows in the greater darkness, only the red of their eyes betraying their presence.

She is naked, and atop her lies the Boy King, rutting like a dog in heat, his pale body looking grey and slug-like as he thrusts into the girl, again, and again while still she stares skywards.

The stars wheel overhead, spinning in their great dance, and still he ruts, as the moon rises over the tallest stone and the altar is bathed in white. The Boy King cries out, just once, and sends his seed into the body beneath before falling, struck prone over her still body.

Finally he rolls off her, and a long cloak is brought to

cover him. The twelve approach and surround him, and he clasps hands with each in turn.

"Go now, and prepare the temple," he says, and two shadows peel away from the rest.

"And what of the girl?" the tall armoured one says.

The Boy King looks back at her, at the still body on the stone.

"Leave her. I will call her back when it is time."

He turns to the remaining ten.

"It is done. The bloodline is secured. Now I can avenge my father and claim my birthright."

The shadows move off, out of Martin's view, but the girl stays, staring silently at the moon, until the sun rises, and a badly bitten man crawls to her from beyond the stones.

And blackness takes Martin, spinning him away from the tableaux which diminish like birds in flight, over the horizon of his conscious thought.

He came awake slowly, aware that he was tired beyond reason, and that there was a dull ache in his left arm that made it too heavy, too solid to lift. Even opening his eyes was proving too much of an effort, so he lay, eyes closed, and wondered where he was, and who belonged to the voices that were murmuring just at the edge of hearing.

"He is strong," one said, and the accent was strange yet familiar at the same time. Thoughts were flying through him, too swift to stop and consider, and he could hang on to none. He should know these voices, but for now he could only listen.

"Aye, that he is. But he has lost a lot of blood, and the wolf has made a sorry mess of his arm. The shock may prove too great, even for the son of the Thane. Check."

The last word had some meaning for Martin, at least. He heard the click of ivory on ivory, and he remembered games played against an old, wrinkled man, games he never won.

"I see your trap," the first voice said. "But I'm afraid you have sprung it too late. Knight to queens bishop three. You see, in one move I block your check, and have either your rook or your queen with the next. You are getting slow, old man—mayhap you are over worried about the lad?"

Chess. He remembered the game, the black against the white, the orders of the pieces and their formalised dances around each other. It seemed he should remember something, about a black king and a white queen, but it had slipped from his mind at the moment of recognising the identity of the players.

He opened his eyes. He was lying in his bed, in his own bedchamber, back in Milecastle. A thin watery light leaked into the room through drawn drapes, and in the corner Menzies and Campbell sat at a small table, the closing stages of a chess match in front of them. Menzies looked distraught, and tugged and worried at his beard while taking large gulps from the mug of wine beside him.

Martin spoke, aware as he did so that his voice was weak, dry and throaty, as if parched for a week or more.

"Surely you have not let yourself be beaten by a barbarian from over the wall? Quick, fetch the board—this could be my only chance of besting you myself."

Menzies and Campbell sprang to their feet, overturning the board and sending the pieces flying. The sight of the white queen lying on her side on the floor almost brought a memory to the surface, but it was sent back when he tried to raise himself, bringing a lancing hot pain along the whole left side of his body.

He looked down, half expecting to see little more than a stump. He well remembered the gouging and tearing his flesh had suffered so he was surprised to see that he still had a left hand.

The white bandages ran the length of his arm, from wrist to shoulder, and patches of red were blossoming there, brought on by his sudden exertion. Martin tried to clench his fist, but the pain was so great that he cried out between clenched teeth.

For all that he must have been thirty years Campbell's elder, Menzies was the first to reach Martin's bed.

"For pity's sake boy, lie still. The wounds are still fresh, and there's nothing apart from my stitches holding your arm together."

"I've seen your stitching before," Martin said through clenched teeth. "When you sewed up the old dog after the boar got him. If you've done half as good a job on me, I'll be grateful."

Martin saw sudden tears in the old man's eyes. He clasped him on the shoulder with his good hand.

"I am strong, old man. And Milecastle and my father will be needing that strength. I'm not planning on dying at any time soon."

At that the old Doctor almost managed a smile.

"And neither am I. It'll be a long time yet before you get the better of me on the chess board."

Menzies helped Martin get himself into the most comfortable position.

"It's good to see you wake, laddie," Campbell said. "Could you manage some ale?"

Martin took a flagon from the Scotsman and downed half of it before he started to choke and splutter, sending a spout of liquid down across the sheets.

Campbell took the ale from him and tutted.

"And there was I thinking I might have made a Scotsman out of you."

Suddenly all three of them were laughing aloud.

"The wolves?" Martin asked, remembering the calls of the pack as they closed in.

"Dispatched by the woodsman," Campbell replied. "When you see him again you must thank him for your life. Although he seems to think that you are of his tribe now, having passed their rite of manhood."

"Aye," Menzies said. "By all means, thank the woodsman, but thank your 'barbarian' friend as much, for it was he who carried you here, over ten leagues distance."

Campbell must have seen the query in Martin's gaze.

"It wasn't so hard. The woodsman's song sustained me. But hush," he said, sensing Martin's growing impatience and need to know. "There will be plenty of time for stories now that you are back with us. Yon wolf made a mess of your arm, and the old man here says that you'll be abed for long days yet."

Menzies was fussing around with the bandages, ensuring they were still tight.

"That's right. I thought we would have to take it off at the shoulder—never have I seen such a wound—but your woodsman friend sang a song over you. 'To empty your soul,' he said. After that he rubbed a handful of herbs into the wound and we managed to save your arm."

"My soul certainly feels empty," Martin said. "But so does my belly. Lennan would not have it so."

"No," Campbell said. "But there are some fresh coneys downstairs that I can fetch soon."

"Wait," Martin said, remembering his dreams and the strength of them. "Tell me more about the woodsman."

"He seemed satisfied with his 'healing', but your arm is sore wounded, and you will never get your full strength back in it," Menzies said.

"I would not be so sure," Martin said, wincing as the doctor tightened the bandage further. "Lennan's herbs, like his songs, are potent and strange. But where is my new friend—I would thank him."

It was Campbell who spoke.

"He has gone back to his woods. He stayed for two days, but complained that the stone walls filled his soul and swallowed his songs. He has returned to his people, but he promised that we would meet again. He has seen it. He also said I had to tell you something, something that would empty your soul. He said that you and the wolf were now together in the wind."

Martin did not need to ask how the woodsman could foresee a future meeting, and he knew better than to try and understand the last statement. But his dreams had been important, he was sure of that, and he was disappointed that Lennan had made no mention of them.

He was about to ask about news of Sean when something Campbell had said sunk through.

"Two days? How long have I been here?"

The doctor gave Campbell a look of disapproval.

"It is four days since you were brought here—near on five since you sustained your wound."

"And they have still not come?" Martin said.

"No," said Campbell. "Although rumours of war have spread far and wide. There are those among the fine people here who would have me flogged as a scaremonger."

"You have told them of our visions in the church?"

Campbell shook his head.

"Only your father, and the doctor here. They counselled quiet, and I am apt to agree with them. I don't want to be tainted with the tag of wizard alongside my already considerable woes."

Campbell had recognised the nature of the people well. Martin knew it—he had been of an opinion with them only a few days previously.

"Let me guess," he said. "Barnstable thinks my father has overreacted, and is questioning the old man's judgment."

"Aye," Menzies replied. "And the people don't want your father to be right, so they do not listen to him."

"They will listen to me, though." Martin said, and had to be restrained from trying to get out of the bed.

"Have you not heard me?" Menzies said. "If you do not rest now, you will certainly lose that arm, and if you lose more blood, you will probably die. Now will you lie still or need I fetch a sleeping potion?"

Menzies had not spoken to Martin in that tone for many years, not since he had been quarantined with swellings in his throat, and that had been more than ten years previously. Suddenly he felt like a child again.

"I'll behave," he said meekly, and Menzies smiled. A smile that turned to a scowl as Martin continued. "But on one condition—you let Campbell here tell the story of how I was saved."

Menzies growled like a small dog when confronted by a stranger, but eventually relented.

"I do not suppose I can stop him. He is as impulsive in

life as he is in chess, but he proved unstoppable there too. He will have to be quick. I go to fetch your father—he has been by your bedside these last four days, and with him I really did have to use the sleeping draught. He would have me flogged if I did not inform him of your awakening."

Menzies left, leaving Campbell and Martin alone. The Scotsman looked strangely embarrassed.

"I am sorry to be the cause of such injury to you," the Scotsman said. "I was lost in the song, and did not notice that you weren't with us."

"Dinnae fash yerself, man." Martin said in an atrocious attempt at a Scottish accent. It had the desired effect, though, for the smile was back on the Scotsman's face.

"And maybe we will make a Scot out of you yet. God knows you're tough enough for it. Any man who can walk away from a fight with an old grey like that one will be welcome in my clan."

"Tell me," Martin said. "Tell me what happened, for I was sure that I was already dead."

"There is not a great deal to tell, for in all truth, I was not present for much of it. Lennan told me later that he heard the wolves calling your name, but all I heard was the song. One minute I was marching along with thoughts of long past summer days in my head, the next I was watching Lennan turn and head back toward me at a run. I barely saw him as he sped past me, heading back along the trail."

Campbell stopped and took a sip from the ale. Martin could smell the bitter hoppiness of it, but he didn't want to repeat the earlier episode so didn't ask to be given any more. He took his pleasure by proxy, watching Campbell take another sip before going on with the story.

"When I finally caught him, he was standing over you, and there were three dead wolves in the clearing. It was obvious that you had dispatched one, and the other two had arrows piercing their hearts. So you see, I missed all the action. I stood there, my heart pounding, my sword in my hand, feeling as useful as a eunuch in a whorehouse."

Martin laughed aloud, then winced at the pain it brought

in his shoulder.

"Sorry, laddie," the Scotsman said with a twinkle in his eye. "I'll moderate my language. At first I thought you were dead, but Lennan was making fast to bind your wounds. There was blood all around you, and I couldn't tell what was yours and what was yon beasties. That was a fine blow you gave it—near cleaved its head in two. You were in a bad way, though. I've seen many a man near death, but few nearer than you."

Campbell stopped then and stared into space. Martin gave him time.

"The woodsman saved you. He sang for you then, and your features softened in repose. He had stopped your bleeding with little more than a few leaves and herbs. I was amazed to see that you were sleeping like a babe. I lifted you, and you felt no heavier than a coney, and Lennan started the song again."

"Almost the next thing I remember is approaching the walls here. Ten leagues in five hours, and carrying a lump like you, yet I suffered no weariness, felt no strain. I sometimes wonder whether the woodsman's magic might not be even stronger than the Boy King's. I certainly like it better."

"I, also." Martin said, and tried to wave his arm, but the strain and agony brought fresh sweat to his brow.

"Hush, laddie," Campbell said. "Lennan's magic might be strong, but stupidity is stronger. Don't undo his good work."

Martin was abashed, and quickly made Campbell go on.

"Yon Barnstable nearly had us spitted with arrows," the Scotsman continued. "Even after he saw it was me. But old Menzies soon put a stop to that. Your Thane was beside himself, and still is. 'Tis a fine man you have for a father, laddie. And here you are, home, unlooked for but safe enough."

"And that is all?" Martin said.

"Apart from this." Campbell took something from a pocket of his waistcoat and placed it in the palm of Martin's good hand. Martin looked down at the large curved incisor of a wolf. There was still some blood and gum tissue at the roots.

"Lennan took it from the mouth of the one you killed. He says that you are a woodsman now, and you need only sing and your new brothers will come to your aid in times of need. He also said that if the stone begins to fill your soul you will find a home in the woods."

Martin felt along the edge of the tooth and shuddered at the memory of how close it had come to tearing out his throat.

"Aye. 'Twas a near thing, lad. But you now have a story to tell your grandchildren. Many men never get that chance."

Campbell clasped Martin by the good hand.

"It pleases me mightily to see you awake and alive," the Scotsman said, and turned and began clearing the floor of the fallen chess pieces, but not before Martin had noticed the tears hidden in the smile.

And his dreams chose that moment to come back to him: full and complete in his memory.

"Wait," he called. "Is there any news of your daughter?"

Campbell turned back and shook his head.

"Sean will have her safe," Martin said, but even as he spoke he was remembering the vision in the church, the brigands and the splash of red on Sean's chest. He was about to speak again when Menzies entered the room, followed by an old, bent figure that Martin realised with shock was his father the Thane.

"No more questions," Menzies said, leading Campbell out of the room. It is time for father and son to be left alone."

"Campbell," Martin said, and the man turned back. "I owe you my life. I won't forget it. But I need a favour."

"Aye?" the man said. "Name it and it shall be done."

"Just don't forget the coneys when you come back. Remember—fill the belly and empty the soul."

The Scotsman smiled, nodded and let the doctor lead him from the room.

As they left, Martin heard Menzies discussing the recent chess game and smiled. Campbell would not get any peace for some hours yet—the old doctor liked his chess, but he liked talking about it even better.

His father brought over a chair and sat beside his bed. The old man had aged drastically in the short week since Martin had seen him last. He looked weak, enfeebled and greatly tired, the furrows on his forehead and around his eyes deeper and longer than Martin remembered them.

He took Martin's right hand and began to stroke it, as if it were a valued pet.

"My boy. My poor boy," he repeated, time after time, tears flowing down both cheeks.

Martin had never seen his father like this. The Thane was strong and strict, almost too strict at times, and such a sign of affection, this late in his life, was proving difficult for Martin to come to terms with.

"Come, Father. I am home, and I am whole. In several days I will be as good as new."

The old man broke down completely, heavy sobs wracking his upper body. Martin took his hand from his father's grasp and clasped him on the shoulder, holding him that way until the sobs subsided.

"Tell me what has happened since I left," he said, hoping that talk would bring his father back to himself.

The old man looked up at him, tears still blinding his eyes.

"I should never have sent you away. The Thane's son should enjoy some privileges, after all."

That was another first. All his life he had been told by his father that he was nothing special compared to the rest, and he had come to act accordingly. If privileges were to be bestowed, his father would make sure that they were shared equally.

He remembered a time not long after he had started his spell on the watch. Barnstable was giving him an especially hard time, and Martin had gone to his father to complain. All he got for his troubles was a clip round the ear.

"The Constable is only doing his duty. If you cannot keep with the pace, then you can leave the watch. And if you leave the watch, you will leave this house. Now what is it to be?"

Martin had gone back to the training, and had even eventually gained a grudging respect from the Constable. But from his father there had been nothing. Until now.

He tried again to get the old man talking, trying to gain time to come to terms with the confusion.

"Come, Father, tell me."

"I'll tell you. But first you will hear me out. I have thought of little else while you lay there. I need to talk to you about your mother, and what happened after she died."

Martin took his hand from his father's shoulder as if he had been burnt by its heat.

"You don't have to..."

The old man interrupted him, and this time there was something of his steel back.

"But I do. Now of all times when there might be only short hours left to us. Just lie quiet. I have been thinking for a long time how to say this. Just let me get it over with."

The old man settled in the chair and rested his chin on his hand in a gesture that Martin long recognised.

"I know I've been hard on you, boy," the Thane said. "And don't try to deny it. You won't remember it, but when you were young, you used to sit on my knee while I held council, and you came with me, hand in hand when we walked the wall, your mother alongside us. But then that day came."

"You do not need to relive it, Father. I know now it was not my fault."

There was amazement on the old man's face. "You blamed yourself? All these years. My poor boy."

He went back to stroking Martin's arm.

"I could not face you. Menzies berated me mightily for it, and came to take my place in your affections. But you see, it was me who sent her out to look after you two boys that day, and it was me who had her maidservant do errands instead of watching by her side. My fault. All my fault. And everywhere I turned, your face was there, reminding me of my perfidy."

Martin once more clasped the old man on the shoulder. Strangely, he could hear Lennan's song in his head as he spoke.

"All is well, Father. You have cleansed your soul, and I could never bear you any ill will."

His father wiped heavy tears away.

"I needed to say it anyway. It has hung on my shoulders for too long. Do you forgive me?"

"There is nothing to forgive," Martin said.

"Yes, there is. But let that be an end to it for now. Do you still want to hear how it has gone in your absence? Or have you had enough of an old man's prattling?"

"In truth," Martin replied, "I don't think you have ever said so much. But I must know."

"I don't know what I would have done without Barnstable this past week," the Thane said. "He has been a tower of strength, while I, old fool that I am, could only sit at my window and worry that I had sent my boy to his death."

There were signs that the tears were about to start again.

"What has our Constable been doing, then?" Martin asked.

"He has been preparing for the coming of the Others. He has mobilised the whole town, and, along with Menzies, has come up with some surprises if they come. Oh, he has had to be hard on some shirkers, but on the whole, he has been the perfect deputy."

And there is the problem, thought Martin. Barnstable would be more than happy to see the old man out of the way. He had always coveted the Thaneship, or rather the power that came with it. And now he had it, in all but name.

Another thought struck Martin. If he had never returned, Barnstable could have claimed the position. He realised that the Constable could prove to be a threat, to his father's well being and his own.

But he didn't want his father following that line of thought—not yet—not while he was in his current weakened state. It was time to change the subject again.

"I have slept a long time, Father," he said. "And I dreamed of great blasphemies."

Deep down in the old man's hooded eyes, he thought he detected a glimmer of interest.

"What? Worse than burning down a perfectly fine barn?" the Thane said, and laughed, a thing which seemed to light up his face and lift years from him. "Come on, boy, tell me, does it involve a woman?"

Martin blushed, and the old man laughed once more, until Martin spoke again, his voice no more than a whisper.

"Aye. It involves women, and Others too. But the worst of all is, it involves our Lord."

He told his dreams to the Thane, while the old man grew ever stiller and quieter, the furrows deepening on his brow once more.

"It seems that the woodsman's herbs do more than heal," he said when Martin was finished. "You have dreamed a tale that few men and only men have ever heard. I myself got it from old Menzies, and he got it from an arcane book locked away in a college in Oxford. But I am loath to tell it, in this place, and this close to nightfall."

Martin pleaded with his father.

"It is important. I feel it. And it has something to do with Sean, and Campbell's daughter."

"Oh yes," the Thane replied. "I am very afraid that it has everything to do with Campbell's daughter."

And the Thane began to tell Martin a story—a father sitting by his son's bedside as the light began to fail.

"I will tell it the way I heard it. But remember, it is only a story, and the Others are renowned liars."

"It starts with a Bible story—our Lord being baptised. Except the Others would have it that the Baptist was one of them, and their king no less. A king in blood but a king without an heir. And the Baptist passed on his arcane secrets, there in the sands of the desert, to one who had been born with power, and later, when the Satan came calling with his temptations of everlasting life and dominion over all, the Lord succumbed.

"And he took to himself twelve disciples, and passed on the teachings of the Baptist. And he took Mary Magdelene to his bed, and a child was conceived. A blood child who was insurance against the line being sundered."

The Thane stopped, interrupted by a sudden commotion from the great hall below, but the noise abated quickly.

"The Constable will deal with it," the old man said before continuing.

"You have seen some of what the Others say happened—the supper and the chalice was an occult ceremony to give their dark power to the unborn child, and the crucifixion was a ruse to allow the Lord, or the Blood King as he now was, to escape from the Romans.

"He and his dark followers went to France. He had gathered a new band, and there were always twelve, and ever he kept Mary Magdelene close, and the day grew closer when the child was due.

"But the Gauls had magic of their own, the magic of the land and the sky, and they battled with the Blood King. Great was the slaughter, and much blood was spilled, but the Gauls finally prevailed. They burnt the Blood King, and Mary, and the child they had ripped from her belly, on a great pyre on a mountaintop. They say the world echoed with their screams for a year and a day afterwards. The chalice they took, and buried it deep beneath one of their temples where their magic could bind it, and they scattered the Blood King's ashes to the wind. And so it ended, for a thousand years."

The old man was interrupted again by the sound of heavy footsteps on the stairs, and Campbell burst into the room, his face flushed and his eyes wide and staring. Martin realised that the man was afraid.

"Sir! I beg you to remember your oath to me. Your Constable has my daughter, and he means to kill her."

The Thane got to his feet, slowly at first, then with more urgency as the Scotsman propelled him towards the door.

Martin made to move, to try to leave the bed, but his father turned and pushed him down. "I can deal with the Constable," he said. "If you would still take commands from your Thane, as an officer of the watch—as a watcher—you are ordered to stay here."

"Hurry, sir," Campbell said. "The mood of your people is ugly." The Scotsman grabbed the Thane and hurried him out of the room.

"What of Sean?" Martin shouted, but they had already

gone.

Suddenly Martin was alone, but he could not lie abed—not when his father and his friend might need him. For the first time in his service he prepared to disobey a direct order from the Thane.

He pushed himself upright, using his good right arm for leverage, but the pain was still almost enough to send him back to oblivion. It was long seconds before he found the strength to swing his legs out of the bed and push himself to a standing position. He swayed alarmingly, and black spots ran in front of his eyes, but he was standing—if he could stand he could walk, and if he could walk, he could get to the hall.

He realised that he was only wearing a long night-shirt, but he knew that he would not have the strength to clothe himself properly, so he took his officer's cloak from its peg behind the door, wrapped himself in it, and headed for the stairs.

Even from the top stair he could hear voices from the hall below, loud voices raised in anger, the loudest of them all from the Constable, Barnstable.

"…and I say she is bitten, and a spy, and she must be burnt, before she brings doom to us all."

Martin descended the stairs slowly, every footstep bringing fresh pain to his arm. Once he missed his footing, and, by reflex, put out his left hand to stop himself from falling. The pain brought him to tears, and he felt new wetness under the bandages, but he kept moving down the stairs.

He could hear his father's voice now. There was no tremor in it, no sign of the old man who had sat by his bed and cried such a short time ago.

"And I gave my oath to this man. You and the whole of Milecastle heard me make it. Would you make me an oath-breaker?"

Martin could hear the anger building in his father, but if the Constable noticed it he didn't pay it any attention. Barnstable snorted, like a disgruntled horse. "The oath means nothing if your ward is a spy. The watch caught her trying to go over the wall. She could have contacted them already—

they may even now be coming here." His voice had risen to a shout and Martin heard the fear there.

"They will come anyway," Campbell said in a soft voice that still carried to Martin.

"And you would know that for certain," Barnstable said. "For surely you are in league with them. If we had not let you enter in the first place, all this might have passed us by."

"Passed us by and gone somewhere else?" the Thane said. "Is this Milecastle's Constable talking? Remember your duty, man—to serve and protect. That means not cringing and hiding like a frightened old woman."

"You will take that back, Thane or no Thane!" Barnstable shouted. "Then we will burn the Other and her father."

Martin turned the last corner, but stood still in the shadow of the doorway. There was a tension in the air, a precursor of violence, and he wanted to keep his presence secret—it might give his father the edge he needed to get out of this situation.

He could see the whole scene in front of him. His father, the doctor, and Campbell were standing with their back to him, in front of his father's great chair. Barnstable and his son were ten feet in front of them, holding the girl between them. She still had that same blank-eyed stare, but she was almost unrecognisable as the girl who had left with Sean.

Her hair was wild and matted, and her clothes hung in torn tatters, offering glimpses of flesh that was caked with mud and grime. Fresh wounds bled, at her feet and hands, and her face was stained deep red all along the lower half, where blood—whether human or animal it was impossible to tell—had dried and flaked.

The old man was talking again.

"But I am still your Thane, and you will still obey when I say that we will not kill her."

"You are the Thane in name only. You have grown weak, old man. Who in the town would nay say me if I took the title? Your pet doctor here? Or this barbarian?" Barnstable said, pointing at Menzies and Campbell. "No. I will not have it. She must burn. She will burn."

And that was when Martin stepped into the room.

Five pairs of eyes turned to look at him, but it was the sixth pair that transfixed him. He had a vision in his head, of a rutting body on a stone altar, but the face on the body was not the Boy King's; it was his own. He forced the image away.

"Lend me your sword, please, Duncan," he said, and the sound of metal on leather as the Scotsman's weapon left its sheath was loud in the sudden silence that had fallen.

Martin took the weapon with a nod of thanks. He knew he was too weak to wield it properly and he would only be able to hold it for a short time, but that was something Barnstable did not know.

Martin called out across the room, deliberately raising his voice so that any listeners beyond the hall might hear:

"My father is the Protector's appointed one, and anyone who says different is speaking sedition. All know that the penalty for sedition is death. Are you ready to die, Barnstable? I have recently killed a wolf so I should have no trouble with a dog."

The Constable went white and stepped backwards. His son was already on his way out of the room.

"Look at her," he said, pleading with Martin. "She is bitten, and she has fed. Are we to let such as this go free?"

"If the Thane wills it," Martin said, and managed to raise the sword closer towards the man. "You spoke treason. Do you wish to repeat it?"

"I have only said what many in the town are saying," Barnstable said, and Martin knew he had already won. There was a cringing, apologetic note in the voice. He realised that Barnstable was, and always would be, a coward who had succeeded through sheer bulk. He also realised that he would never be frightened of this man again.

"Then send them to me," Martin said. "And I will re-educate them. Now leave the girl and go—the Thane has questions to ask her that are for his ears only."

Barnstable looked like he might protest, but Martin made a step closer to him, his sword extended, and the Constable released the girl. His face showed how little he liked it, but he left to meet his son at the door, both walking backwards out of the hall, their eyes never leaving the sword in Martin's hand.

It was only after the great doors had shut behind them that Martin let himself slump. The Scotsman was the first at his side, and Martin fell, exhausted, against Campbell's shoulder as the Scotsman took the sword out of his hand.

"That was nobly done, my friend. You are truly your father's son, and I am once more in your debt."

"Aye," Menzies said. "But if this lad is not back in bed soon, he will not live to see it paid. Help me get him back upstairs."

"No. You see to the girl," The Thane said. "I will see to my son."

There were fresh tears in the old man's eyes as he moved closer to Martin.

"You have disobeyed your Thane, boy."

"I know," Martin said, "but my father needed me."

"That he did," the old man said, getting hold of Martin under his good arm. "And your father is very glad you came."

Campbell and the Thane almost carried Martin back to his bedchamber, but in truth, Martin, although weak, felt better than he knew he should. He should not have been able to even lift a sword, never mind face down a man many years his senior—a man he had feared most of his life. The woodsman's herbs were potent indeed, and he thought that the arm would heal better than Menzies could ever imagine.

The doctor followed them up the stairs, leading the girl, who followed him, as docile as a lamb.

Menzies took charge when they reached the chamber. He stripped the cloak off Martin's shoulders, and almost cried out when the bandages were revealed—what had been white was now blood red and sodden.

They got Martin back into bed as quickly as he was able, and started stripping the matted dressings. Fine beads of sweat formed on Martin's brow as they were removed and he passed out once as the wounds were cleaned. Menzies said nothing throughout this operation, and Martin knew his arm was bad.

"I had to do it," he said to Menzies. "You would have thought less of me if I hadn't tried."

"Maybe," Menzies muttered. "Now hold still. This is going to hurt."

Martin only looked down at the wounds once, then had to look quickly away. His arm looked strangely shrunken, as if whole muscles had been stripped out, and the flesh was the colour of raw steak, crisscrossed with the black catgut that Menzies used for thread.

Fresh bandages were applied and tightened, bringing more sweat and more clenched teeth, and the procedure finally ended with Menzies ordering Martin to stay in bed. The doctor made sure that Martin was not going to move before seeing to the girl.

She stood in front of him, but did not recognise his presence as he looked deep into her eyes and checked that the blood around her mouth did not come from any major wound. Then he looked over the many cuts and abrasions on her body.

"She is hurt, but not badly," the doctor finally said. "With your leave, my Thane, I will take her next door and tend to the wounds."

The Thane nodded and Menzies led the girl by the hand.

"Clean her up at the same time, as a favour to me." Campbell said. "She was always a tidy girl, and it pains me greatly to see her in this state."

Menzies headed for the door which led to the room where Martin bathed. He was almost through the door when Martin spoke.

"And what about the child?" Martin said. "Does it thrive?"

From the sudden quiet that fell, he surmised that his guess had been correct—the others had all known already.

"It thrives," Menzies said. "And as far as I am able to tell, it is still man and only man—the ceremony has not yet taken place."

At that the doctor left the room, leading the girl by the

hand.

"What ceremony?" Martin asked. "And if she is here, where is Sean?"

"Your second question I cannot answer," his father said. "But I fear the worst. As to the first, it concerns the end of the story we began earlier. But it can wait—you must sleep."

"I have slept for long days," Martin said. "And I promise to stay abed awhile. Just tell me the rest of it—I have a feeling that she is very important."

"She is," Campbell said. "But she is also still my daughter. I brought her here in the hopes that she could be kept free from the designs of the Boy King, but look—she has returned—and now she is closer to him than ever."

Campbell wiped a tear from his eye.

"Forgive me. I need a drink. I shall go and fetch some ale—I believe we would all benefit," he said. Then he too left the room, leaving Martin once more alone with his father.

"I have raised a son to be proud of," the old man said. "You are going to have some trouble with the Constable from now on, but even he still respects the Thaneship and the order of its succession. And that is what the rest of our story concerns—the order of succession of the Blood King."

The old man settled himself in the chair by the bedside and began to talk. Martin closed his eyes and imagined the story unfolding there in the dark, and at some point the tale became dream, but he could not tell when one ended and the other began.

"One thousand years after the chalice disappeared, it was found again. But first, we must go back several decades, to the Holy Land. The Templar Knights were searchers after power, any power that would give them something to fight the strength of the Pope with whom they were always at odds with. And they found it, there in the desert, protected by a sect of crazed monks— the severed head of the Baptist, a head that still dripped fresh blood a millennium after it was struck from his body at the whim of a woman. And from that moment on, the return of a Blood King was inevitable, if not so simple to achieve.

"Some say that the head spoke then, promising them dominion; others say that they had access to centuries old occult lore from the old man of the mountain that let them access its latent power. However they managed it, they discovered the whereabouts of the chalice, buried deep beneath an ancient chapel in Southern France. As you have seen in your dream, they brought it up out of the ground. And they collected the blood of the Baptist, and mixed it with their own. And then they drank it from the chalice, and no more were they men and only men. The Others had come back into the world."

The old man stopped talking as Campbell returned with a pitcher of ale and some mugs. They were all silent as the ale was poured. For a second, in the dim light, it looked like the Scotsman was pouring blood from the pitcher, but the illusion soon faded as the Thane continued. Campbell sat behind the old man, idly pushing chess pieces around the board, taking regular gulps from his mug, and regular refills from the pitcher.

"The Baptist had promised them dominion, and for a while they had that, their power growing nightly, their dark shadow stretching over much of Southern France. But they grew too bold too quickly, for it was difficult for them to keep their true nature secret from men and only men. In time they came to the attention of the Pope and the French King. And again there was great slaughter in the southern mountains. Many of the Others were slain, and many more taken to deep cells within the Vatican, where they were tortured in silver chains until they revealed their secrets. But neither the chalice nor the head of the Baptist was ever found."

The Thane paused to take a drink.

"Now we come closer to how the tale intertwines with our lives," he said, and was about to continue when Martin put up his hand to stop him.

"I believe I know some of the next part," he said. "The Bruce gave them sanctuary, and they helped him win at Bannock Burn."

"I see your education was not totally wasted, then," the

old man said. Martin felt himself blush, and caught a broad wink from Campbell over his father's shoulder.

"Aye. And after Bannockburn, when St Clair, the oldest of them, was made Steward, and the thirty had already become three thousand, the Baptist's head whispered to them of caution and of the need for a royal bloodline to cement their authority in years to come. And Bruce gave the Others lands, around the old fort at Edinburgh, and the prisoners from Edward's army as slaves and as food.

"And over the years the Others grew stronger, but they could not find a royal line to bind them to the throne. They had dominion over most of the land north of the wall, but they yearned for more, for fresh conquests, fresh blood, for the birthright they felt was their due. After Bruce's death, St Clair declared himself Stuart, and king, and there were none left who would rebel against him. He built a great castle on Edinburgh rock, a symbol of his power, and he had a dark temple built there to house the twin treasures of his brotherhood. It is said that dark deeds were practiced there, but the Blood King, the creature that St Clair had become, yet had no heir.

"And finally, the Baptist who is known amongst the Others as Baphomet, announced that they were strong enough, that the time was ready. St Clair took to wife a young girl whose offspring would have claim, not just to the throne of Scotland by right, but that of England as well. Of course the lineage of the father was deliberately confused, as England would never accept an Other as their sovereign, and Mary, Queen of Scots, was never accepted in England in her own lifetime, but nine months later, Charles Stuart ripped himself out of his mother's womb to claim his birthright.

"But here is the part that concerns us. It is written that after she had conceived, Mary was thereafter in thrall to the Blood King, and she had no life of her own save that which he gave her. It is also written that the child must not be turned before its eighth month, lest it kill the mother too early."

"So there is a chance to save her, then?" Martin said.

It was Campbell who replied.

"A chance. Aye. But that's all there is. It seems that the Blood King drives her even now, for how else would she have returned here? He has called her, for he needs to keep her safe for the ceremony."

"That is twice a ceremony has been mentioned." Martin said, remembering his dream. "Has it anything to do with the chalice?"

"It has everything to do with the chalice," the Thane said. "That is the source of all that they are. It is said that the chalice was forged in the days of Moses, and that the first Others were in the exodus but refused to take the commandments. However they started, though, they need the chalice for the ritual."

"Aye," Campbell said bitterly. "And a dark ritual it must be. It is said that the Blood King turns the babe with the aid of the chalice and the head of the Baptist. But there is no man and only man who has ever been present. Whatever is done, it will happen in yon temple in Edinburgh, of that I'm certain. And unless the Boy King can be defeated, it will happen in March of next year."

"Can we not do something?" Martin said. "Can the doctor not get rid of the babe?"

"Get rid of the babe? And kill the mother? No. She can be restored—that was the reason I brought her here—the other I could have done myself weeks ago if that were an option."

Martin suddenly noticed that the Scotsman was drunk, and that the pitcher of ale was rolling empty on the floor beneath him.

He spoke softly to the man.

"As I am your friend, I swear to you that the Boy King shall not have her. I will die first."

Campbell moved over to Martin's side, weaving slightly, and clasped him by the good arm.

"If it comes to that, we will die together," he said. "And we will take Charles Stuart's pup with us."

Martin turned to his father.

"And what happened next?" he asked, then realised he

already knew. Every schoolboy was told of the coming of the Stuart King, of his cunning in hiding his true nature, of his eventual betrayal of his position and how the Old Protector overthrew him and had him staked in front of the populace at the tower.

And every schoolboy told tales, ever enlarging the facts, of the Boy King who had been left in waiting, Charles Stuart's insurance, and the heir to the vacant throne. The story of his first attempt to reclaim it, when he was stopped only by the burning he received in the Great Fire, was a popular one around all fires in England.

Many were convinced that the terror had perished there in London, but there had been persistent rumours that he was gathering his twelve again, and would make another attempt on the throne. It seemed that the rumours had been right.

"So what do we do now?" Martin asked. The Scotsman had sat done again and was slumped back in his seat looking ready for sleep, and the Thane had his head in his hands.

The old man looked up at Martin, and was about to speak, when the room echoed to the sound of the great bell in the tower above and the castle was suddenly full of the sounds of rushing footsteps and screams.

They heard footsteps running up the stairs, a messenger coming to tell them the news that Martin already knew.

The Boy King had come to reclaim his bride.

CHAPTER 7

2nd NOVEMBER, 1745 FAR SAWREY, LAKE WINDERMERE

Sean awoke with a splitting headache and the taste of dead leaves in his mouth. He had to wet his left eye with spittle to clear out the gum that held it closed. His back felt like it had taken several sharp kicks from a man in heavy boots and the soles of his feet were like red-hot irons.

The sun was only just up, and he had managed a mere four hours sleep, all that he would allow himself before setting out on the trail again. He was leg weary, and sore from numerous aches and pains as he started on the third day of his chase.

In that time he had slept only ten hours, and his body was beginning to rebel. When he had set out from Garstang he was sure that he would catch her quickly, and once, on that first night, he had caught a glimpse of her in the distance, her white dress standing out in the moonlight. But then the sound of hoof beats had sent him off the path, and he had been forced to wait in hiding as the Warden and his men passed. By the time he was back on the path, she was long gone.

The Warden had not found her either, for he had spotted him and his men less than an hour later, camped out on the trail. He had passed them in a wide circle and kept moving north, and since that first night, he had not seen or heard the officers. He hoped they had given up, but the Warden did not seem like a man who would take kindly to losing a prisoner, particularly one who had killed one of his own. He feared that he would be seeing the big man again.

Neither had he any further sight of Mary Campbell, although he had spoken to people who had marked her passing. Only last night he had met a family travelling south from Carlisle who had seen her—far off and on a hilltop— still heading north. They had taken her for an apparition, and the wife of the family he spoke to had prayed all through the conversation.

He had met many people travelling away from the wall. Rumours of the Boy King's return were rife; he had an army of Others recruited in the American Colonies; he had gained great supernatural powers through a pact with Satan; his father had returned from the true death to fight with him; the French Navy had landed at Arbroath; the Protector had fled the country. But none of the rumours affected him so much as the thought of what had been done to Mary Campbell—the single tangible bit of evidence he had that proved to him beyond doubt that the Boy King was evil incarnate.

Last night he had fallen asleep, dead on his feet, with little or no regard for his surroundings. He had only stopped when he realised that he had been walking but asleep for a good two hours. He remembered moving off the road and finding a secluded spot, then he had fallen like a man shot and was asleep in seconds. On awakening, he took his bearings, and was surprised to see that he was less than two hundred yards from an inn. That proved to him something he had suspected during the night—he had strayed from the path he was following. The girl seemed to be returning the way they had come, and they had not passed such an inn on the outward journey. He dimly remembered a crossroads some ten miles back, but he had been so tired then that his feet had carried him on the easier downward track rather than upwards to the high tops they had travelled before.

Too much time had been lost—he had to get back on her trail soon, or she would be over the wall and gone before he could catch her. And catch her he would. He vowed it on all that he held holy. He stretched and popped out the pains in his spine before stepping back onto the road.

The inn sat square on a crossroads near the edge of a large body of water which Sean knew was one of the lakes, but had no idea which one.

One arm of the road led down to a small jetty where boatmen were already loading passengers and goods onto small boats, but making little impact on a queue that was growing steadily.

The other arm of the road wound away from the lake and steadily up a long hill into the distance. Even though it was still early in the morning, there was a great deal of traffic, all of it heading South.

The inn looked a prosperous one, and one doing good trade for so early in the day at that. Outside the whitewashed walls three high passenger carriages were drawn up, their roofs piled with trunks and hand baggage—some of the more well off denizens of Carlisle making their escape, no doubt. Beside the carriages were the simpler transports of poorer folk, cattle, donkeys and ponies overburdened with goods, rickety carts which had seen better days carrying all the worldly possessions of their owners. Small children, bemused and afraid, were running beneath the wheels of the grander carriages, and a well-dressed man was trying to keep them away, making ineffectual swipes at them with a riding crop.

Local hawkers had already spotted the potential of a new market, and there were small stalls set up on makeshift tables selling pies, bread and sausages. Although it was just past dawn, the inn looked to have been in business all night, and there was a group of ruddy-faced individuals gathered in the doorway, already much the worse for drink. Sean noticed too late that they had spotted him.

He realised what he must look like to them. He had been walking for two days, trudging through muck and briar, and he'd had no thought for cleanliness. His legs were caked with mud up over his knees and his clothing, what remained of it, hung in tattered scraps from his body, which was now a good deal thinner than it had been just a week ago. He had not shaved during that week, and the new growth of beard felt dirty and itchy. He had run his hand through his hair just seconds before, and knew that, amid the tangles, there were small twigs, reminders of bushes that he had pushed his way through in his attempts to stay hidden from the road. He smelled rank, although his nose had long since adjusted to it. He had become a person that a week ago he would have averted his eyes to avoid.

The drunkards however had no such scruples.

"Hey, lads. Here comes a right one." This from a man who himself had only one tooth left of his upper set, and a wart so large on his cheek that it looked like he was growing a second nose. Sean refrained from the obvious comment. He didn't want to inflame them—at least, not until he got closer and found out whether they were armed.

"Look at the state of him. What do you say? Shall we give him a bath?" another said, and they all laughed in that too-loud way that comes with a surfeit of ale.

"Aye. I think a trip to the lake is called for—it will take that much water to get him clean."

The group found this uproariously funny, and brayed with laughter again. They reminded Sean of a group of piglets at a trough.

Five of them moved away from their positions in front of the inn and started coming down the road towards him. Two were none too steady on their feet, but there was one, a big fellow with a mass of red hair, whose eyes were clear and bright with the excitement of a fight. He had met this one's type before—William Barnstable being a prime example—big and full of bluster in a crowd, always a ringleader when he knew there was someone to back him up. Sean knew just how to deal with him.

He hunched down, as if cowering, and affected a high-pitched whine to his voice.

"Spare me a penny, good sirs. A penny for a loaf of bread to sustain me on this fine morning."

The red-haired man was by now standing just in front of Sean, hands on his hips—he obviously thought of himself as a dispenser of wisdom and justice, lord of his own tiny domain.

"A penny, is it? Well, beggar, we have got something much more valuable for you—we have a lesson to teach you," he said, and swung a huge fist at Sean's head.

Sean ducked under the blow and grabbed the man's arm by the wrist, using his opponent's momentum to swing him round and, at the point furthest into the swing, gave a sharp tug. He smiled to himself as he felt the man's shoulder come away from the joint, accompanied by a loud squeal of pain, but he didn't have time to gloat, for two more were on him quickly.

The first, a short, squat fellow, grabbed Sean in a bear hug. Sean almost recoiled from the smell of stale beer that emerged from the man's mouth, but even before his opponent started squeezing, Sean dug his thumbs into the man's eyes and twisted, hard. He saw blood spurt under his fingers before the pressure released and he was dropped, the man falling away from him, squealing and sobbing, runnels of red running from between the hands covering his face.

The third man managed to throw a punch while Sean was still recovering his balance, and it knocked him to his knees. His attacker moved in closer and aimed a kick at Sean's head, but Sean turned and in one smooth movement grabbed the man's ankle and twisted, pulling his attacker to the ground where it was an easy matter to put him out of commission with a swift rabbit punch to the head.

Not even out of breath, Sean stood and looked for the other two. He had nothing to fear there— one was being violently sick at the roadside, and the other stood, like a rabbit hypnotised by a stoat, his eyes staring at Sean while his hands twitched and trembled like a marionette in the charge of a drunk puppet master. Sean took one step towards him and he ran, heading off down the road away from the inn.

The red-haired man was in retreat, heading for the jetty, his right arm hanging strangely loose by his side, and the one whose eyes he had gouged was sitting in the middle of the road, mewling like a baby. The fifth was still out cold on the ground at Sean's feet.

"They have been spoiling for a fight all night," a voice said from the side of the inn. "And I'd say they've found one."

Sean turned to see a stocky figure watching him. The man was totally bald, his head almost perfectly round. His belly hung over the top of his trousers as if trying to escape from his vest, but his shoulders were broad and his chest deep. A single gold earring glistened in his left ear and he had a small, neatly trimmed beard, clean-shaven at the cheeks. His eyes were a deep sea blue, and there was no guile there as he scrutinised Sean.

"I'd say you're a bit more than the beggar you seem," he said.

He held a mug of ale in his right hand. Of his left, there was only a stump, the remaining skin puckered and scarred from a severe trauma. He saw Sean looking and held the stump up.

"Lost it in the Carib. Some bastard Corsair blew it off with a musket at close range." He came forward and handed Sean the mug of ale.

"Take this, it looks like you need it. And come inside and we'll get you cleaned up. We can't have a good fighting man like yourself going around like the green man."

Sean took the ale gratefully, gulping half of it down before the man had a chance to change his mind. The alcohol, on an empty stomach, immediately started a buzzing in his head, and he reminded himself to be careful—it wouldn't take much to get him into the same state as the men he had just dispatched, and although this man seemed friendly, he remembered how quickly the butcher in Garstang had turned against him.

"But won't the landlord complain? I am no fit sight for the fine customers from yon carriages," Sean said, pointing at the front of the inn where a small crowd was just dispersing, no doubt disappointed that the fight was over so quickly.

"Those 'fine people' have seen worse than you this past night," the man said. "I fear that this is not the genteel ale house they expected when they stopped. And as to whether the landlord will complain—I don't think so," he said, putting out his good hand for Sean to shake. "John Fitzsimmons is the name, proprietor of this fine establishment. Now come in and have a wash and we'll see about getting you some clean clothes."

Sean eyed the man over the top of the ale mug. There was still no guile in those eyes, but brigands existed in many forms, not just those one met on the open highway.

"But I have no money, and I must be going—she may be

far away already."

Sean realised that he had spoken out of turn, but fatigue, the fight and the sudden effect of alcohol on his brain had dulled the quickness of his mind.

Fitzsimmons put his finger to his mouth to quiet Sean, and leaned closer to him, speaking low so that no one else could hear.

"I have seen her, if I read you right. And you are not so far behind her as you fear. Now come. You will bathe and eat, and all I ask in return is to hear your story, although I know more of it already than you might think."

Sean allowed himself to be led into the tavern, his head spinning at the implications of what the man said.

The inside of the tavern was so dark that Sean's eyes had trouble adjusting, but his nose wasn't as numbed as he'd thought—the smell of stale beer, smoke and urine told him immediately he was in a tavern. It was a smell that reminded him so much of home, of Milecastle, that he had a hitch in his chest that he could only disguise by taking another sip of ale.

The main barroom was low of ceiling, and hung thick with the smoke of many pipes. There were more than thirty people inside, all jostling for the attention of two barwomen who, even at this early stage of the day, looked tired and stressed.

"Get yerself over here and sell some beer, you old bastard," one of the women shouted. At first Sean thought she was talking to him, but the man beside him shouted back.

"Sell it yourself. I have a guest."

The woman left four flagons of ale at the table nearest her and came over to stand in front of Sean.

"A guest is it? And what makes you think I'd let such as this in my bar?" she said. Sean was reminded of the fisherman's wife—there was something of the same fire in her eyes.

"I beg your pardon, Madam..."

"Madam is it?" she said, but something in his voice had softened her.

Before Sean could speak, Fitzsimmons butted in.

"He just put Gregory's arm out of joint, and Jack Tarvit is out cold out in the road. He's done us a favour."

She looked Sean up and down.

"He doesn't look capable." But she was smiling as she spoke. "Take him through the back. And make sure he washes. The stink will linger for days."

Fitzsimmons led him through the bar to a small room at the back. A fire was roaring in the grate, and the sweltering heat of it made Sean step back.

"Sorry," Fitzsimmons said. "I got a taste for warmth in my years of service, and the old stump cries out for it when it gets damp. It does mean hot water, though."

There was a black iron kettle hanging over the fire, and Fitzsimmons emptied it into a washbowl before inviting Sean to use it. He didn't need a second offer.

Mud and grime sloughed off his skin, and when he was finally clean Sean was embarrassed at the state in which he had left the washcloths.

"Don't worry," said Fitzsimmons. "The missus has seen worse in her time. Now what can I give you to wear?"

He went to a large sailor's chest in the corner of the room and began to rummage around inside it. He came back to Sean with a pile of clothing.

"Try some of these on. I was a bigger lad than you, and they are old, but most is of good quality and you should find something serviceable. Now forgive me, but the missus will hamstring me if I don't get out there and give her a hand. I'll fetch you some grub when I get a chance."

Standing in front of the fire, Sean stripped off his tattered clothing and dumped it in a bundle at his feet. Given the state of it, he was surprised it didn't move off of its own accord. Now that he was washed, the stink of it stung his nostrils. He took it to the fire and dumped the rancid pile on top of the burning logs. The cloth burnt blue and sent a puff of dark smoke up the small chimney, but all was soon consumed. He waited until the last scraps turned to ash before turning back to the chest.

The innkeeper had been right about the clothes. There

were fine silks, in gaudy colours that made Sean think of hot climes and bright sunshine, and braided jackets of military issue. Under that there were shirts bedecked with frills and trousers in bold checks, but most of the clothing seemed too outlandish to his rural tastes. He could not imagine the innkeeper ever wearing much of it either, and wondered where such garments might have come from.

There were even women's dresses, heavy and long in taffeta and silk—not the kind of thing that Sean was used to seeing womenfolk wearing. More what he imagined for the papists across the channel in France, or beyond the wall in the north.

In the end he chose a simple pair of heavy grey woolen trousers, with a thick linen shirt and a leather vest to replace the old one. It was in deep red leather, and rather gaudy, but the leather was supple and uncracked, and it did not restrict his movement.

Among the clothing he discovered a pair of soft leather boots, and to his surprise they fitted him perfectly, although they came a bit high up towards his knee for his comfort. He noticed as he dressed that the wound in his shoulder was nearly healed—he had almost forgotten it, as he had also forgotten the episode with the brigands. They seemed already like memories from a distant past, things that had happened to another person.

He wondered if the innkeeper felt the same way about his time before he was innkeeper. For the first time he really looked around the small room. The walls were paneled in dark oak, and shelves and alcoves had been fashioned along all four walls. The reason why was obvious—the innkeeper had been a sea-faring man, and curios and mementoes lined every available surface. Sean was particularly drawn to the carvings: intricate workmanship on pure white bone, scenes of tall ships in cliffy harbours, of swaying trees and dusky maidens.

But there was more; a ship's compass that had obviously taken a blow from a heavy blade, a flintlock pistol whose movement was corroded and jammed, a beaded necklace cunningly wrought from pieces of shell and pearl, and a small arsenal of bladed weapons—swords, cutlasses, knifes and bayonets—some showing signs of rust, but in the main, well tended and shining like the day they were made.

One particular sword caught Sean's eye. It was a blade in the Spanish style, with a gauntlet cover for the hand cunningly cut into a spider-web pattern, plated in fine silver, but strong enough to give protection. The blade itself was beautifully balanced, and it sang as it passed through the air as Sean tried some cuts.

"I see you have found my spoils of war," the innkeeper said from behind him. "It is a fine blade. Best Toledo steel. No, keep it beside you for the time being," he said, as he saw Sean moving to put the sword back.

He handed Sean a large pork pie, still piping hot. Sean put the sword on the chair beside him and took the pie, having to shuffle it from hand to hand to avoid being burnt. The smell of it made his mouth fill with saliva, and when he bit into it, he believed he had never tasted anything sweeter.

"The missus makes them herself out the back and we've sold more in the last three days than we have in the past year. I think you've made an impression on her, for she will not charge you for it."

Fitzsimmons watched in amusement as Sean devoured the pie in four or five bites.

"Sorry," Sean said as he finished the pie, wiping the crumbs from his mouth. "But it is a while since I ate more than berries."

"That was obvious," the fat man said.

"I have also taken some of your clothing," Sean said. "But I fear much of it is too gaudy, even for my liking."

"Aye. Clothes for warmer climes, most of them. My collection has a story to tell," he said, motioning Sean towards a chair. "But it is your story we are concerned with today. Let me tell you what I know of it and you can fill in the blanks—it will be faster that way. But first, something to lubricate the thrapple."

The man left, and Sean was surprised how nimble and light he was on his feet. He had seen men who moved like that before, men who knew how to fence, and how to handle themselves. He was glad he hadn't had to fight the innkeeper—it would have been a lot closer than he would have liked.

Fitzsimmons returned only seconds later and thrust a mug of ale into Sean's hand before he spoke, Sean becoming ever more incredulous with each word.

"You left Garstang three nights ago, in pursuit of a woman who walks yet seems to be dead. You came from the north originally—my guess is Milecastle or one of the other forts—and you are in some way responsible for this woman. The story goes that the woman brutally killed an officer in Garstang, and the Warden of that town and his men are scouring the countryside looking for both of you. You have chased the woman north since then, sleeping rough, but you don't know how far ahead of you she is. Close enough for you?"

Sean nodded. There was only one way Fitzsimmons could have come by this information.

"The big man was here, then?"

"Aye. Just last night. With fifteen men. They drank a lot of my ale, and left without a penny payment. The missus was fit to split herself with apoplexy."

The innkeeper laughed at the memory.

"Aye. She is not a woman I would cross," Sean said.

"You don't know the half of it," Fitzsimmons said. "I had to hold her back—she was going for the big man with one of my sabres."

"The Warden struck me as an honest man," Sean said.

"I suppose he is—he gave me a note to deliver to Garstang for recovery of my monies. But it is not from him I know of the woman. I saw her this morning, barely half an hour before you showed up."

"I got ahead of her," Sean said, almost to himself. "She must have passed while I was sleeping, less than three yards from the road."

"Aye. She was on the road all right. I only caught a glimpse of her myself," Fitzsimmons said. "I was emptying a chamberpot when I saw a white form come gliding out of the dark. Gave me a fair shock, it did, what with those eyes and that stare. She walked straight past me without even a nod, and it was only when I got back in and had some ale inside me that I realised that she was like some I had seen in the Carib, their minds enslaved to another. Am I right?"

Sean nodded, but said no more.

"Ah, a close man. I can see there are more stories yet in you."

Fitzsimmons stood.

"You may wonder why I do not turn you in to the Warden's men? The truth is, there has been no glamour, no adventure in my life since this," he said, waving the stump. "You remind me of the boy I once was—the one who left Lancaster at sixteen to take to the seas."

"I am indebted to you," Sean said. "I met a man in Garstang who would have turned me in for a leg of venison, and you have restored my faith in man's nature."

The fat man bowed from the waist.

"I give you the clothes, and I give you the sword. Just promise to come back and tell me the whole story once it is over. It'll be something to liven up the dark winter nights, I'll wager."

Sean nodded, afraid to speak, overcome by the simple generosity of this man.

The innkeeper found him a belt and scabbard for the sword from the depths of his sea chest, then led him back out through the bar.

Fitzsimmons' wife was standing behind a long low bar-table. She whistled when she caught sight of Sean.

"He cleans up well," Fitzsimmons said.

"That he does," she said. "And the clothes look better on him than they ever did on you." She smiled as she said it, and winked at her husband. She was not like the fisherwife after all, Sean thought. This one would not betray her husband.

And he realised something else: He would no longer be sleeping with other men's wives. The part of him that led him to that pass had gone, lost sometime in the past week.

"I thank you, Madam..." he said, and this time she blushed and giggled, so that one could see the girl she had once been. "..for the food, the hot water, and the clothing. I will be back to repay you ere too long."

"Aye. Do that lad. And we'll find a wench to keep you warm when you return."

Now it was Sean's turn to blush, and Fitzsimmons ushered him outside to save him further embarrassment.

The yard in front of the inn was nearly empty now, and the carriages had all departed from outside. There was no sign of the five whom Sean had bested earlier.

"There'll be more folk along later this afternoon—the ones who have left Carlisle this morning. The missus will be up to her elbows in pork fat what with all the pies we'll be needing," Fitzsimmons said, before turning to Sean, his eyes suddenly sombre. "Your tale has to do with the reason those people are moving south? It is tied in with everything that is happening, does it not?"

Sean merely nodded.

"Then go, then," the innkeeper said. "And God speed you."

Sean buckled the sheathed sword at his waist and clasped the man's good hand.

"I am forever in your debt. And if I am able, I will return and drink your inn empty while relating the story."

Fitzsimmons laughed, and for the first time in many days, Sean joined him.

"A fighting man, a close man, and a drinking man. I look forward to meeting you again, young sir."

"Sean. Sean Grant is the name," Sean said, and the innkeeper bellowed again.

"Well maybe not so close after all. Now get you going. You are more than an hour behind now, but I believe we have improved your chances."

Sean agreed with him.

"And if you come across an old cove called Menzies in Milecastle," Fitzsimmons said, "Tell him that Fitzsimmons' stump still itches."

"I can see that I am not the only one with stories yet to tell," Sean said, and the innkeeper merely smiled.

"Stories start and end in strange places, and some people are given to appear in more than one," he said. "If Menzies has not told his, then it is not my place. Bring him back with you if you can. Then we will have a night, no, a weekend, to remember. Mayhap you will get him and I drunk enough to tell you our tales of the Carib."

"By the time old Menzies is drunk, I am already too far gone to notice," Sean said, and Fitzsimmons laughed again and smacked him on the back.

"Practice, my boy. Years and years of it. Now be off with you."

Sean clasped hands with the innkeeper once more, then headed off along the north road, and when he next looked back the inn was lost to view.

His new boots felt like he'd been wearing them all his life, so comfortable were they, and he had not realised what a difference a wash and a change of clothes would make to his mood. He realised that the meeting with Fitzsimmons had contributed to his good humour—his faith in human nature had been restored and he had been lifted out of a black pit of despair.

He would have to remember to ask Menzies about Fitzsimmons—he had a feeling there was a story worth telling there. He realised he knew almost nothing about the doctor's history—he was merely part of the day to day fabric of life in Milecastle. Oh, the old man knew almost everything there was to know about everything, but he never gave away anything about himself. He was as close with his story as he was in his chess games. Sean wasn't even sure that the Thane knew.

But all of that would have to wait. Mary Campbell was ahead of him, and he meant to catch her. He started to walk faster, until he was almost running.

Although winter was nearly here, the day was sunny and nearly warm, and he worked up a sweat under the heavy trousers and shirt. It was almost a relief an hour later when the road started to rise away from the lake, the air becoming chillier as he headed for the higher hills which marked the northern end of the range.

He continued to walk fast, half expecting at any moment to come upon Mary Campbell, sitting at the roadside, just waiting for him to catch up. But the morning wore on, and he had no sight of her, nor any indication that she had even passed this way.

The path wended its way high up over the tops where the wind blew icy cold, and now he began to worry, for in the last glimpse he had been given of her, he had seen that she was only wearing a thin dress, and no shoes on her feet. Surely she must have stopped to seek shelter by now?

But he didn't believe it. Whoever, or whatever, wanted her, wanted her as soon as possible— that was obvious by the way she was being driven. He walked on, trying to pick up the pace as a fine sleet began to fall.

By early afternoon he was wet through, cold and miserable, all trace of his good humour utterly vanished. He was walking along a high ridge, exposed to the elements, and he had passed no one on the road for over an hour. Sleet bit at his cheeks, and he was now grateful for the fine growth of beard at his cheeks. He began to suspect that he had taken a wrong turning, and seriously considered turning back to the last crossroads, some four miles behind him.

Then the path turned around a high spar of rock and the ground fell away beneath him. He stood, right at the edge of the range of hills, looking over the flat ground towards Carlisle.

The sleet seemed to be confined to the other side of the hill, and here the sun shone out of a nearly clear sky. Way over to the west the sea gleamed brightly, but to the north, over Carlisle and beyond, heavy black clouds hung menacingly low, their bottoms scraping on the hills, rain or sleet laying a sheet of grey that obscured everything beneath.

And out there on the plain an exodus was in progress. About a mile from where he stood, at the foot of the hill, was the head of a long drawn out train of refugees that stretched all the way back to Carlisle itself, some fifteen miles in the distance. He could see carts overloaded with goods, whole families on foot, and even farmers driving their cattle and sheep before them. It looked like the whole of the population of the surrounding area was on the move.

Mary Campbell would not be on this road, he was sure of that. The path they had used coming south was some five miles east of his current position, and that was where he suspected she would be. He scanned the area, but there was no sign of movement. He was able to pick out a path to follow that would enable him to get away from the convoy that was headed towards him, and he headed down the hill fast.

He managed to keep out of sight of the travellers, and by the time he got to the bottom of the hill and turned away from the road, the first of them was already mounting the first rise.

Fitzsimmons would have more custom than he could handle in a few hours' time. The memory of the pork pie was just that, a memory of food that his stomach had long forgotten. It grumbled at him occasionally, but he chose to ignore it for the time being—he could ill afford time that would allow his quarry to get further away.

He wondered if there were Milecastle folk amongst the convoy that was now wending its way up the hill. Indeed, he wondered if Milecastle still stood, but he put it to the back of his mind—his duty for now was to Mary Campbell.

His first sign that he was on the right track came half an hour later. He was crossing a patch of muddy ground when something caught his eye, a splash of colour. He looked down to find a small patch of blood, still fresh. And beside it, slowly filling with stagnant water, a pair of footprints made by someone travelling barefooted, someone travelling north. With renewed vigour he headed along the path.

He began to recognise the area he was passing through and, sure that he was now on the right road, began to walk faster until he was almost running again.

He was almost upon a small copse of trees that he recognised as the spot where he had dispatched the brigands when he heard voices from ahead of him.

There were raised voices, high, not with fear but with excitement. Sean was able to make out three separate men. Using the trees and undergrowth as cover, he skirted around until he had a view into the clearing beyond.

There were three of them, all right, and they were trying to wrestle Mary Campbell to the ground. He could tell by their tunics that they were the Warden's men, but there was no sign of the big man, and for that Sean was grateful, for he didn't want to face the Warden in a fight.

Three horses were tethered to the same tree that Sean and the girl had slept under, and Sean allowed himself a grim smile as he noticed that the men's muskets were still in their harnesses beside the horses' necks.

The sight of Mary Campbell filled him with dismay. Her skirt was tattered and torn, and her legs below the ankles were a mass of bruises and small cuts. Mud caked her from head to foot, and her hair was a tangled mass of twigs and leaves. Only the eyes reminded him of the girl as he had first seen her by the gates of Milecastle.

The lower half of her face was obscured by blood, and at first he thought she was wounded before he noticed that one of the men holding her down was streaming blood from the side of his head, and that half of his ear seemed to be lost.

It looked to Sean as if he had arrived only seconds after the men had found her. The blood on her face was fresh and the wound on the man's ear was bleeding more profusely by the second. Mary Campbell was fighting like a cornered cat and her nails raked one of the men's cheeks, bringing a splutter of expletives. He hit the woman, hard, sending her down off her feet. Two of the men managed to finally get their weight on top of her, holding her to the ground.

"Hold the bitch down," the one with the bloody ear said, fumbling with his trousers. "She needs to be taught her place."

One of the others, a smaller, thinner man, stepped away from the prone girl.

"The Warden's orders were to return her unharmed."

"I'm not going to harm her, just show her where her place is. Hold her down, I told you."

The wounded man finally got his belt unfastened and dropped his trousers. Sean could contain himself no longer. He stepped from the bushes and advanced on the three. They all had their backs turned to him, and did not see or hear him until he was only six feet away.

His sword was in his hand, and the men were within range, but he could not take anyone, however base and ignoble, with a stroke to the back. The watch had taught him to kill Others, but stabbing men and only men in the back was another matter. He was thinking about the body of the small boy back there in the copse as he spoke.

"If there are lessons being taught, then I am willing to learn," he said.

The men spun on their heels, the wounded one helping Sean's cause by tripping over the trousers that were down round his ankles. The man lost his footing and, falling sideways, disturbed the balance of the man to his left.

Sean concentrated on the man on the right. It was the thin-faced man who had spoken earlier. He was already drawing a sword as Sean moved in. The man slashed at him, and Sean parried, aware already that the man was no swordsman. He feinted to go under the man's sword, then twisted his wrist and went over. The Spanish steel felt like an extension of Sean's arm as it slid through the man's throat and, with a twitch of the wrist, sliced his jugular and sent him gurgling redly to the ground.

Sean sensed a movement to his left, and turned and ducked in one movement as a sword flashed over the top of his head. His third adversary was still trying to get his trousers buckled, but the second man had regained his balance and was advancing on Sean, sword swinging wildly. Again, this was no swordsman, but he was big and fast and Sean had to retreat under the onslaught. Over the man's shoulder he could see the girl rise and get to her feet. Their eyes met, but there was no recognition there as she backed away. Sean had no time to watch her further as the big man came at him, his heavy sword sending shocks up Sean's arm every time he had to parry.

The third man had regained his composure, and was at the point of drawing his own sword. Sean had to finish this fast, and get after Mary before she got away from him again.

The big man drew his sword back to swing at him again, and Sean stepped inside the swing, cramping the man's movements and at the same time smashing the pommel of his sword into the man's face, feeling the small bones in the nose crush wetly with the force of the blow. The big man let out a yell, but he managed to push Sean away from him, and came back swinging. Sean let him come, and, just as the sword seemed set to cleave his skull, stepped to one side. The momentum of the man's swing carried him forward and off balance, and Sean thrust his blade deep into the man's side, at the same time kicking him over to the ground. The man tried to raise his sword, but a final blow, with the flat of the blade to the side of his head, put him out of the fight.

He had no time to think. The third man had advanced, and was snarling at him, like a cornered wildcat.

"Fancy blade-work, boy. Let's see if you're as good as you think you are."

Sean noticed with dismay that the man carried himself like a true swordsman. This one wasn't about to rush in swinging. He circled the man, saying nothing, trying to stay calm, trying not to think of Mary Campbell getting further away with every movement.

"That's two fine men you've dispatched there, boy. I don't think the Warden will admonish me if I send you to join them."

The man sent his blade out in a quicksilver flicker that Sean only just managed to parry as it was over his heart. Still he didn't speak.

"Saving your breath? That's fine by me. It'll be all the sweeter when—"

Sean didn't give him time to finish the sentence. He stepped forward into a lunge that caught the man off guard, but his opponent managed to weave to one side and the stroke cut a slice across his ribs instead of taking him through the heart. The man let out a yell and stepped into the attack with renewed vigour so that Sean was hard pressed to defend himself.

The sound of clashing steel echoed around the clearing as they circled, each searching for an opening. Sean was painfully aware that he was weakening faster than his opponent, and decided to try a risky feint, one that he had sometimes had success with on the training ground.

He stepped backwards, as if retreating before the attack, and let his right leg give under him, feigning a stumble and letting his sword hand go down towards the ground, looking as if he was going to use it to steady himself. As he'd hoped, the man went for his suddenly exposed left hand side. Sean ignored the descending blade, and, with a straight arm, he punched his sword upwards, catching his opponent under the ribs and pushing through to cleave his heart. The man fell, already a dead weight, pinning Sean to the ground, and he had to use all his remaining strength to push the body off and stand upright.

Suddenly there was no sound in the clearing. Sean was breathing heavily, and he had to examine himself twice to make sure that he was not himself wounded. His legs trembled beneath him, and his hands shook as he walked unsteadily over towards the man he'd felled with the flat of his sword. He too was dead, his entrails showing pink at his side where the first stroke had cut deep. Sean leaned away from the man and vomited the little there was in his stomach into the long grass.

He had only just stood upright when one of the tethered horses whinnied, and there was an answering whinny from nearby. He heard the sound of hoof beats, and they were close. He only had two options; run or hide. The horses sounded too close to allow him time to run, and he could think of only one place suitable to hide.

The three brigand's bodies were still where he had left them, although something, or someone, had tried to pull one of the bodies out from under the bushes. He only had time to notice that there were fresh bite marks on one of the youth's legs, and wonder what Mary Campbell had been doing when the Warden's men found her, before he heard horses entering the clearing behind him. He dived into the undergrowth and pulled the bodies over him, trying hard not to gag at the stench, or to scream as the large black flies crawled over his face.

It didn't take them long to find his hiding place. He heard voices coming ever closer.

"They must have been ambushed by brigands," one voice said.

"Ambushed, my arse," a voice replied. "Brigands don't leave clothes and weapons behind. And brigands generally use muskets, not swords. Do you think that Johnson would be bested at swordplay by a common brigand? He'd fought with the Protector in Ireland, that one. He knew how to handle himself."

The voices were almost on top of him now. He tightened his grip on the sword, but it was lying partially underneath his body and he wouldn't be able to find much use for it in such a confined space. He held his breath and turned his face to the ground, trying to keep the tremors from taking over.

Something fell over his face. He groped at it and felt his fingers touch the cold hand of a dead man. He had to bite his tongue to stifle the sudden instinct to scream.

"In Jesu's name, what's that smell?" the first voice said.

He heard the sound of branches rustling as the foliage was moved above him, and he was close enough to hear the men's breathing.

"Leave it," the second voice said. "They've been dead a while, and by the look of them, this lot were actually brigands. I'd say they got what they deserved."

"Shall we tell the Warden?" the first said.

"What, and have him send us running around the countryside even more? No. Forget it. Cover them up. The one we're searching for is not here."

"But the Warden said to search everywhere."

"Do you want to touch those?" the second voice asked,

and there was disgust in his voice.

Five seconds later the sound of rustling came again, and footsteps receded into the distance before Sean felt able to take a breath, a deep whooping thing that almost gagged him as the taste of death filled his mouth.

He crawled further into the undergrowth, trying to put distance between him and the bodies, but he was brought up tight against a briar, and could escape neither the stench nor the flies that buzzed incessantly around his head. He stayed that way for a long time, caught between the desire to be after Mary Campbell and the need to avoid capture. He had a sudden vision of the dead crawling through the bushes towards him, dead eyes accusing, and he clamped his eyes tightly shut.

He had now killed six people, and that would have to be paid for at some point. He knew that the Warden would not give up now, and that he would surely be hanged if caught, but he had sworn an oath to Campbell, and he intended to honour it, even if it brought his own death in the process.

There, under the bushes with the bodies of those he had killed, he made a vow. Only let him get Mary Campbell safe and well again, then he would hand himself over and take the consequences.

He heard muffled voices in the distance but could not make out what was being said, and he dared not try to move closer. It was many minutes before he heard the sound of hoof beats from the clearing as the Warden's men departed, and even then it was five minutes more before he started crawling out of the undergrowth, keeping his eyes shut to avoid having to see those bodies again. He crawled on his belly and peered out into the clearing beyond, but it was now empty, only the bloodstains on the ground left as evidence that the fight had ever occurred.

He pulled himself out of the bushes, having to struggle to get free of some blackthorn. He swung the sword, and managed to get rid of some of the offending branches, but still something tugged at him. He had a bad moment when he could see in his mind's eye the dead hand of a brigand dragging at his heel, intent on pulling him back down to join the family, but he was in sunlight now, and such thoughts had little hold on him. He tugged hard, and felt the woolen trousers rip, then he was free to pull himself out and stand in the fresh air.

A breath had never tasted so sweet, but he had little time to savour it. He had lost nearly an hour, and now he had to be careful not to be seen by the Warden's men. A quick survey of the clearing showed him that he was alone, and that the Warden and his men had indeed taken their dead with them. For that Sean was grateful, for he didn't think he could look at those again without the guilt making him throw himself on the Warden's mercy.

He spent three minutes he could scarcely afford just making sure that Mary Campbell was not in hiding somewhere in the area, but once he had satisfied himself, he headed north with never a look back.

The sun was already beginning to sink in the west. He pressed on, running as fast as he could while studying the ground in search of the marks of bare feet. He saw nothing.

By dusk he reached a hill overlooking Carlisle, having seen neither Mary Campbell nor the Warden's men. The weather had closed in again, heavy sleeting rain coming from the north, an incessant battering in his face.

A mile away, partially obscured by heavy cloud, Carlisle itself looked dead and deserted. Only the light from half a dozen fires showed that anyone still remained there. The best part of the populace seemed to have fled.

Not for the first time, Sean thought about what he might be headed towards. There might be no Milecastle left—everyone he had ever known in his life could already be gone. But that he could not believe, would not allow himself to believe.

He thought about heading for one of those points of light. There he might find food and some warmth. But although he was tired and leg weary, he forced himself to press on in a lonely trek over now-familiar roads. He was only a few miles from home, and if he did not find Mary Campbell before then, at least he could eat in his own halls and dress in his own clothes before resuming the chase.

And still there was no sign of her, or of the Warden and his men. Indeed the night was now so dark that he might have passed within ten yards of either and missed them completely.

If he hadn't known some of the landmarks on the road, Sean could easily have become lost. Again he marvelled at the power that could command Mary Campbell over so many miles and drive her with such accuracy when she seemed senseless.

At some point the rain stopped, and stars twinkled into being overhead, but the path was still sodden and heavy, and he was making slow progress. The fine leather boots were now caked with over an inch of clinging black mud.

The night drew on endlessly until he was finally less than a mile from Milecastle. Many a time he had cursed those pale towers, and the stone walls that had always seemed more like a prison than a home, but tonight he almost wept tears of joy at the sight. He was so cold, and so hungry that he no longer thought of his vow or his chase. All that concerned him at that moment was getting dry and getting some warm food inside him.

He headed down into the valley. From four hundred yards from the wall he could see that there were guards there still, and more than normal—the watchers at least were made of sterner stuff than the citizens of Carlisle.

He was wondering whether Martin had returned yet when he heard the sound of distant hoof beats on the road behind him. He broke into a run, just as the hoof beats were drowned out by the tolling of the watch bell.

CHAPTER 8

3rd NOVEMBER, 1745 MILECASTLE

Martin's bedchamber was suddenly thrown into turmoil. The Thane's head shot back as if he had been struck, and for the first time in his life, Martin saw fear there, a fear that was quickly replaced by a steely determination.

"So. It has come at last. Would that it had been twenty years since."

The bells tolled again and Campbell sat bolt upright in his chair, confused and bewildered at the means of his awakening. Menzies appeared at a run from the adjoining chamber and everyone began speaking at once until the Thane shouted above the noise of the bell.

"Quiet. I will have quiet."

His voice, trained over many years in the Great Hall, brooked no argument and the room fell silent.

"Menzies. You know what to do."

"Yes, sir. The men are ready. But Barnstable has charge—I could stay with you."

"You know as well as I do that the men won't follow him in battle—your place is at the wall," the Thane said, and pointed at the door.

"Yes, sir," Menzies said and began to move. Just at that moment the messenger finally arrived at the top of the stairs, out of breath and red in the face.

"The Others. They have come," he managed to blurt out, before suddenly busting into tears.

"We know that, man," Menzies said. "Get to your post. We need every man out on the walls." The doctor pushed the man back through the doorway before making to leave himself.

"And...old friend?" the Thane said, "Take care. We have more chess to play yet."

The doctor nodded and left. Martin thought he looked strangely happy, as if he was looking forward to what was to come.

His father ran his fingers through his hair and stared blankly at the wall for long seconds before muttering to himself.

"After all this time, it has finally come."

He shook his head, as if to clear away the fear that Martin could see in his eyes, and turned to the Scotsman.

"Campbell. I have a favour to ask of you," the Thane said.

"You took me in when no one else would, and you have kept your word. Ask, and I will give."

"You asked me to protect your child, now I ask you to protect mine," the Thane said.

"I had hoped to fight by your side, sir," the Scotsman said. "The Others have sore hurt my family and I would like to repay some of that pain."

"I think you'll have a chance, if not this night, then soon. But I must have a man I trust here to watch my son and your daughter. And, although we are only of brief acquaintance, there is no man I trust more."

Martin started to protest, but a look from his father stopped him.

Campbell no longer seemed the worse for drink. His eyes were clear and he stiffened his back as he stood from the chair. He removed his sword and held it in front of him in a salute.

"I shall guard the lad as I would my own," he said. "You have my word on that."

The Thane embraced the Scotsman.

"And you have mine. When this is over we will share some ale and tell some stories and leave the young ones to the fighting."

"I can think of no better way to spend my retirement," the Scotsman said.

The Thane turned to leave.

"Father," Martin called out. "Wait. I am an officer of the Watch. My place too is on the wall."

He tried to raise himself from the bed, but he was too weak. His earlier exertions had taken what little remained of his strength, and he could not get as far as swinging his legs from the bed.

The old man looked at him and managed a small smile.

"You are excused your duty tonight. I must go—the Thane's place is with the watch on a night such as this."

He leaned across the bed and took Martin by the good hand.

"I feel in my heart that you have a part left to play in this mummery. Do not be so quick to rush on stage—this is only the first act."

Martin grasped his father's hand with all his strength. There was so much he needed to say, about his youth, about his mother—of whom they had never until tonight spoken—and of his now- found realisation of the burdens the old man laboured under, but all he could do was grip harder and let tears run down his cheeks.

"Be careful, Father." Martin said, but the old man merely smiled again and left the room. Martin had a sudden premonition of doom and feared that he would never see the old man alive again.

Campbell saw his look.

"Don't worry. The fort is well defended, and old Menzies has cooked up a few tricks that'll keep the dark ones busy. They won't find the taking of this place easy."

But for all the bravado, Martin could see the doubt in the man's eyes, and the screams he could hear over the tolling of the bell seemed to give a lie to his confidence.

The bell suddenly stopped, and in its absence the sounds of battle could be clearly heard. The clash of steel, the roar of muskets, and, most prominent of all, the screams and wails of men and only men confronted with the dark evil of the Others.

"At least give me a sword in my hand," he said to Campbell.

"Let me check on the girl first," the Scotsman said. "Do I have your promise that you will stay there?"

Martin nodded. In truth he knew that he would not be able to even stand, never mind fight, but the thought of his family, his friends, facing the Others without him, chafed sore, and hot tears rose in his eyes with every new scream.

"She sleeps," Campbell said, returning from the adjoining room. He carried Martin's sword which he placed on the bed beside Martin's right hand.

The Scotsman suddenly looked solemn, his face as rigid as if carved from granite.

"If they get past me, I want you to kill the girl," he said.

Martin must have looked horrified.

"It is the only way," Campbell said. "And it will go better for her that way. Do I have your word?"

Martin nodded, suddenly unable to speak. He had to force the words out.

"You have my word that I will try," he said. He hoped the Scotsman didn't hear the lack of conviction in his voice. Faced with Mary Campbell's blue eyes, he would be more likely to clasp her to him than to kill her.

"That is good enough for me," the Scotsman said. "Although I have a feeling in my bones that I will be meeting Lennan again. Tonight is not my time."

Martin wished he shared Campbell's confidence. He had a sick feeling in the pit of his stomach and his injured arm was throbbing as if someone was gripping it tight, about once every two seconds.

"I should be out there on the walls," Martin said.

"Aye," the Scotsman responded. "But we each have been given our orders. For now we can only wait."

He took position in front of the door to the bedchamber, his sword in his hand.

Sean ran towards the South Gate of the fort. He was moving as fast as he could, faster than he ever had in his life. His breath caught in his throat, and his heart felt that it might jump out of his chest, but the horses behind him were catching up too fast—he was not going to make it to the walls.

He stopped on the road and waited, leaving his sword sheathed at his side when he realised there were more than ten horses bearing down on him.

The Warden was the first to reach him. He pulled his horse up and dismounted some five yards away. He pulled a pistol from his belt and advanced towards Sean.

"Can you give me a good reason why I should not shoot you where you stand? You have much to answer for, young sir," the Warden said.

The big man's hand was shaking, so much so that Sean wondered if this was the first time the man had pointed the weapon at another human being. He decided he didn't want to test the Warden's resolve.

"Aye, and answer I will. You can take me away in as many chains as you can muster," Sean replied. "But first I must go to the aid of my people. The great bell has been tolled. The Boy King has come."

The Warden looked over Sean's shoulder. His eyes widened and the blood drained from his face. Sean turned to follow the gaze, and his heart fell.

A black shadow crawled along the east side of the fort, a shadow made up of a horde of dark figures that moved almost too quickly for the eye to follow. They were inside the wall!

White flashes burst from the castle walls, followed immediately by the sharp popping of musket shots. A shock wave ran through the dark horde, stopping it for a second before it surged forward again. The first screams carried over the field towards them.

"Help me," Sean said. "Help them."

He made to run, but the Warden stepped in and held him back.

"This is not our fight," he replied. "Do not be so quick to rush to your death."

Sean struggled in the big man's grip, but the man was as strong as he looked and he was unable to break away.

"If we don't try to stop them, it will be everybody's death soon enough. Do you think the Boy King will stop here? How long will it be until he is at your door? And who will you ask for help then?" he said, almost shouting now. "Quickly, we have little time."

The Warden seemed to come to some decision and turned to speak to his men.

"It looks like we have blundered into a fight," he said. "I will go to help the people there. Is anyone with me?"

He gave them the choice, and four of them turned and fled, their horses carrying them away as fast as they had come.

"I will deal with you later," the Warden said to Sean. "But for the present it seems we must fight together. Now how do we get in without getting ourselves killed?"

Sean surveyed the scene around the fort. The black shadows swarmed to the east in great numbers, but somehow, by a miracle, they had failed to breach the fort. He could see that it would only be a matter of time, though, for their numbers were too great to be repelled by the small force mustered against them.

"The South Gate," Sean said. "And if that is closed against us, then we will have to go over the wall and pray we are not mistaken for enemies."

The Warden gave Sean a riderless horse.

"It belonged to Johnson, one of those you left dead in yon clearing," he said, without an intonation in his voice.

As soon as Sean was saddled, the Warden led the band forward, galloping towards the besieged fort.

Sean's heart sank as he rode. All of their drilling, all of their exercises, had been based on the one fact—that the wall would not be breached. He could imagine the fear and trepidation in the hearts of the defenders. He kicked the horse forward, trying to wring every last bit of speed from it.

Ahead of them a small group of shadows detached themselves from the main group and were already creeping around the corner to the south side. Sean could see no defenders on the wall above the South Gate and spurred his horse forward ever faster, drawing his sword as he approached.

He was amongst them before they noticed his coming, and his first sword stroke took one in the neck and passed clean through. The headless body dropped away from him as two more quickly filled the space. Pale hands grasped at him, and yellowed fangs tried to reach his legs, but his sword was a whirling sliver of death, and his momentum carried him through to the gate where he turned the horse so that his back was to the wall.

A shadow leapt at him, catching him on the left hand side and threatening to drag him from the horse as it climbed up his body. The horse bucked and thrashed under him, rebelling against the strangeness of the Others. Using his knees, he tried to keep the horse turned so that his back was to the wall. He felt twin fangs bite deep into his shoulder just above the collarbone before he twisted and hit the creature in the face with the hilt of his sword.

He was not prepared for the reaction—the creature screamed, a high whine that reverberated in his ears for long after, and it fell away from him, its head smoking, burnt patches of flesh sloughing off its ruined face. The hilt of Sean's sword glowed briefly white, then subsided. Fitzsimmons had been right, it was a fine blade—there were not many swords that had pure silver in their pommel.

Three more of the Others stood around his horse, but they had backed away from him, hissing like snakes, their eyes blazing fury. These had passed the first death many years ago. Their flesh was waxy and yellow, almost green. Their clothes, or what remained of it, hung off them in tatters. They were wild and feral, all trace of what had once made them men and only men long since gone.

They circled the horse warily, but did not seem inclined to come closer. Sean showed them the sword hilt, and they backed off. Not far, but at least it bought him several seconds. His horse still bucked and kicked beneath him, but he managed to keep control of it as he banged on the door of the gate with his sword.

"Ho! Fellows of the Watch. There are friends here who need entry," he shouted at the top of his voice, but there was no reply.

More Others had come from their left, as if drawn by the

fighting. The Warden was pushing his horse through the throng towards him, and there were three more horsemen behind him. Small, knotted tangles of heaving shadows on the ground showed where the remainder of the warden's men had fallen.

"We should make a run for it," the big man shouted as he clubbed a ragged, almost skeletal, figure aside. "One more minute and we're dead men."

Sean shook his head, even as the creatures re-grouped and began to close in around them. They were even more cautious now, their approach slow and deliberate. Their eyes shone red in the darkness, and some were already daubed red with the blood of the Warden's men.

All the horses were shying and kicking, terrified beyond control.

"Dismount," the Warden shouted. "At least we can let the horses save themselves."

The five men stood in a tight knot beneath the gate as they released the horses. The Others pounced on the fleeing animals, like dogs on a fox. Two of the horses went down, hamstrung. They were immediately covered in a sprawling, hissing blanket of shadows, and thankfully the piteous noises from the stricken animals was quickly cut short. The others were lost from sight in the night, but the screams of triumph from out in the dark spoke of their fate.

The Warden's own horse, a great brute of a beast, still stood, lips pulled back from bared teeth. An Other hung from its neck, fangs seeking the jugular, while a second tried to grab the beast's back legs. The horse reared, shaking its neck, dislodging the Other which fell under the flailing hooves, one of which came down hard on the Other's head, caving it in on one side. But still the Other managed to grab at the leg, unbalancing the beast. Immediately two Others jumped on its back, and, although the horse managed to bite the fingers off one, still it couldn't stop itself being dragged to the ground.

The Warden took aim with his pistol and shot it between the eyes, but still the Others fell on it in droves. Sean saw tears in the big man's eyes before he turned back to the gate.

Sean pounded on the great oak door again.

"Men of the Watch, to me!"

But still there was no response, and the men backed against the door as the snarling shadows crept closer around them.

"The only way to bring them down is either to take their heads off or with a strike through the heart," Sean said. "Let's see how many we can take with us."

The Warden nodded grimly as the first creature leapt from the throng and threw itself at him. Sean had to admit he was impressed as the officer took the Other by the throat and wrenched, removing its head from the body and tossing the torso back among its brethren before kicking the head to join it.

"Will that do?" he said to Sean, and there was a sparkle in his eyes that Sean hoped never to have directed at him.

Sean barely had time to signal his approval before the rest of the Others moved forward. One was faster than the rest and Sean stepped into its path to meet it. He drew back his sword to strike, and was already bringing the weapon down when he was drenched by a spray of water from above.

The liquid fell on his head and ran off his shoulders, stinging his eyes, but the Other fell to the ground writhing and spitting, its flesh bubbling and boiling like a slug doused in salt. Its limbs thrashed in the mud, thrashings which got less frantic until they finally stopped, leaving only an oily puddle of grease behind on the ground.

The rest of the shadows backed off, hissing louder than before.

A voice came from above them.

"Open the door. Quickly!"

Sean looked up to see old Menzies standing on top of the wall. He was holding what appeared to be a massive pair of bellows, like those which would be used to keep a fire going. The old doctor squeezed the handles of the bellows together and Sean finally saw their use. A jet of water arced out of the spout, flying high over the men's heads and falling onto the Others. The water immediately sent them into a frenzy as they struggled to back off even as their skin boiled and seethed. The smell of garlic was heavy in the air.

The heavy gate was pulled open behind them, just wide enough for one man to slip in at a time. Sean allowed the Warden's men to go first, and there was only him and the Warden left when the jet of water faltered overhead, first to a dribble, then stopping all together.

"Another barrel!" he heard the doctor shout, but didn't have time to wonder what he meant as the remaining Others lunged forward.

He pushed the Warden inside just as they were on him. Remembering the effect from before he pushed the pommel of his sword into the nearest one's face, at the same time kicking out at one who had come in low around his ankles. He felt teeth scrape at his foot, and was grateful to Fitzsimmons once more as the leather boots saved him further damage. The one who had taken the blow of the hilt fell away, but others were already taking its place. Sean caught hold of the one nearest him, and, turning and spinning in one movement, he threw himself through the open door, carrying the creature along with him.

He heard the gate slam behind him, but had no time to look around. The Other spun away from him, then came back, faster than a cat. He had no time to raise his sword, no time to do other than react. His body remembered its training and his hands shot up, catching the creature around the neck, his arms straining to keep clashing fangs away from his jugular.

Then suddenly he was drenched again, and he felt his hands slide over the Other's flesh as it sloughed away from under his fingers. He gagged as the stench of rotting meat filled his mouth and nose. Then he was holding little more than a loose jelly which fell through his hands and slid to the ground.

He looked up to see Menzies smiling down at him, the large bellows poised in his hands. Sean could now see that a flexible pipe made of soft leather stretched from the back of the bellows and into a large oak barrel on top of the wall. The stench of garlic was everywhere.

"Well met, young guardsman! How do you like my water musket?" the doctor shouted. Sean started to reply when the great bell suddenly went quiet and the sound of fighting slowly died away. A great silence fell on Milecastle.

High in the watchtower Martin realised that all noises of fighting had stopped. A deadly silence fell outside as if the castle was shrouded in thick, deep fog. And suddenly he knew what was happening—he had seen it all back in Newcastleton in the woodsman's fire. The Boy King would be coming forward with his dark companions. He would stop, and look up to the sky, as if half- expecting to see someone floating there.

There was a doubling in Martin's mind. Although he still lay on the bed, part of him was once more out above the fort. Once again he saw the crescent moon, and once again the darkness took note of him, and the Boy King bent his mind towards him.

"Where is my bride?" a voice commanded in his head. He was powerless to resist as a string of pictures formed in his mind. He saw Mary Campbell as she was when he first saw her, her departure with Sean, her standing in the Great Hall with Barnstable's hands on her—that picture lingered longer than the rest—and finally, peacefully asleep in the adjoining room.

Although he hadn't moved from the bed, he could see that Menzies had done a good job of cleaning her up. She was wearing one of his old nightshirts, and her hair, newly combed, lay on the bed like silk. Martin felt a pang of desire, and a voice chuckled in his head.

"No. She is already spoken for. But maybe I'll give her to you when she has fulfilled her destiny, although I don't think you will find her quite so pretty by then."

The voice chuckled again. "Now bring her to me."

Martin felt a spasm run through his body and his legs twitched violently, but even the Boy King's mentalist powers were not strong enough to overcome the fatigue in his limbs.

He heard a snort of disgust and felt the parasite mind depart, looking for a new prey to subdue.

"Are you all right, lad?" Campbell said, noticing Martin's sudden distress, but Martin waved him away, back to his position by the door.

"He knows where she is," he said. "He'll be coming. Don't trust anyone."

Campbell didn't waste time asking questions. His stance grew straighter and more alert as he moved closer to the door.

The silence went on, and Martin could almost believe it had been a dream. Almost.

His muscles continued to twitch and his lower legs jumped as if he were a dog dreaming of chasing rabbits. He was nauseous, his head light. He closed his eyes, but felt like he was spinning down through a vortex and opened them again to see Campbell watching him, concerned.

"Are you well, laddie," he asked again.

"I've been better," Martin said. "But I'll live. Watch the door. It will come soon."

"You have seen him again?" the Scotsman asked. "He is here?"

"Aye. He is here. Now be still, it'll be on us sooner than we wish."

The Scotsman turned back to the door once more, and Martin lay quiet until his muscles felt like his own again. He still felt as weak as a lamb. How was he going to prevent this monster getting to Mary Campbell if her father fell?

Sean was also thinking of Mary Campbell as he ran across the main quadrangle in the centre of the fort.

He was heading for the east wall. He had been surprised to find that the girl was actually here, having half expected to find that she was already over the wall and out of his reach. Menzies had assured him she was safe and with her father, which probably meant that he was free of his oath, but he would not rest easy until she was well, could look at him with those eyes and recognise him.

But for now his place was on the wall with the rest of the

guard. Menzies had quickly shown him the operation of the bellows, ten of which had been placed at strategic places on the walls. During the last attack they had been the only things that kept the Others at bay, but the water was already running low and even now, all over the fort, garlic was being crushed into what remaining supply of water could be found. The barrels on the wall were being replenished, by bucket, gourd and anything else that could be used to carry liquid.

He ran alongside the Warden, the pair of them heading for the east wall where the fighting had been thickest.

"Maybe they have drawn back," Sean said, noting the silence that still hung over the town. All he could hear was the sound of their footsteps and their breathing.

"No," said the Warden who ran beside him. "They are still there. Can you not feel it?"

And in truth, he could, a dark place in his soul that chattered and gibbered, demanding attention. Join us, the voices said. Join us and be free.

But Sean wasn't tempted—he'd seen what happened to those who joined.

"If I fall, bitten, you will do the right thing by me?" he said.

"What—and lose the chance of a public hanging?" The Warden gave out a hollow laugh. "I doubt if either of us will survive this night, but I promise you a quick dispatching, whatever way it falls. Good enough?"

"Good enough," Sean said, and was surprised to see that the big man was smiling.

"Now let us kill some of the dark ones. After chasing you all over the country, I'm itching for a decent fight."

As they approached the wall, they saw the carnage that the last assault had wrought. Bodies lay strewn on the ground, and the women of the town were going amongst them, armed with hammers and stakes, searching for those who had been bitten. And when they found one, they cried, in recognition and in sorrow, before driving a stake through the heart and passing on to the next.

Some of the Others had made it over the wall, but

Menzies' water cannon had caught them, and Sean had to be careful where to place his feet to avoid the steaming, oily puddles of gore.

The stench was like nothing he had ever encountered, and even breathing through his mouth did little to help. The only saving grace was the fact that he had not eaten.

The Warden wasn't so lucky. Sean stepped out of his way as the big man lurched to one side, covering his mouth. Sean averted his eyes, but could do nothing about the hollow, retching sounds from behind. He moved away, trying to put some distance between them.

As he mounted the short flight of stairs to the wall, he met the Constable Barnstable coming down, but there was no recognition in the man's eyes, only a blank stare.

"How goes it?" Sean asked. But the Constable pushed passed him, almost knocking him off the narrow staircase.

"Master William? Are you well?" he asked, grabbing at the man's shoulder.

The man turned, and again Sean saw no recognition in his eyes as his mouth raised in a cold smile.

"I have never felt better," the Constable said, and laughed from deep in his chest. It was a sound Sean had never before heard issued from the big man's mouth. He could only stand, slack- jawed in amazement and watch as Barnstable headed away over the quadrangle. Sean saw the Thane notice the Constable and follow some yards behind, his sword drawn, but he had no time to wonder at the reason as the silence finally broke.

Out there beyond the wall a drone started, low pitched at first, but rising ever higher until a tune was just recognisable, the battle pipes of old Scotland rousing the dark clans to battle.

The scene that met him when he reached the top of the wall was worse than the most frightening of his childhood nightmares. The black shadows milled in a throng that blackened the field for as far as he could see, a horde of Others that included men, women and children, all grist to the Boy King's mill. Amid the Others, men and only men walked, but men with the same blank stare he was so used to seeing in Mary Campbell, men who carried muskets and wielded broadswords.

Sean had heard of such as these—slaves employed to protect the Boy King in daylight hours, and to go places where the Others would not. Such as these would not be affected by the liquid, and he wondered how long it would be before they were the ones attacking the wall. But maybe they had been part of that first attack, for from what Sean could see, the protective chain of bulbs was already gone, torn from its place by force.

Out there, two hundred yards away, sat a patch of greater darkness from which ripples of movement seemed to run as if a great black spider was sitting in the middle of a web, manipulating the whole structure with twitches of its legs.

As he looked at that greater blackness, Sean felt a twinge in the bite in his shoulder, but that was soon forgotten as the black horde crashed against the wall.

Two of Menzies' bellows were being deployed along this stretch, and Sean pulled rank to take charge of one of them. The Warden followed him and took charge of the second.

He was just in time. The Others were crawling up the wall as if it were horizontal, their eyes gleaming red in the dark, heavy drools of saliva running from their mouths.

They were a rag-tag bunch for an army. From his vantage point Sean saw kilted Scotsmen, the red-tunics of those who had once been in the English army, the tattered woolen over garments of farm workers, and, down there, just beginning to climb, the recently animated bodies of fellow officers of the watch killed in the last attack. They made up little more than a screaming, disorganised, mob; men, women and older children all united in just one common cause—to get over the wall and feed.

He aimed the nozzle of the bellows down at them and pressed the handles together. The stench of garlic suddenly filled his nose and brought tears to his eyes.

As the water hit the attackers, they fell back, hissing and mewling, leaving long trails of greasy marks as they slid back to the earth. Screams rent the air, inhuman screeches of pain. Some of them, only their heads touched by the liquid, kept trying to climb until being hosed down further. And still the throng pressed forward, walking over the bodies of the fallen. And everywhere that water touched it brought boiling lesions to the skin and fresh screams in the air.

"This is no way for a man to fight!" the Warden shouted, and Sean had to agree with him, but anything that killed the Others so efficiently was welcome at a time like this.

He saw that the Warden was managing to pump nearly double the volume of water that he was capable of; the huge muscles of his shoulders and arms bunched and knotted tight under his overshirt. The Others had fallen in their scores below him and he was now beginning to create an empty buffer zone. However, the enemy was getting smarter, and more of them were moving in Sean's direction, where the flow of the killing liquid was less.

"Close up!" Sean shouted, and the Warden moved nearer. Sean kept pumping water down over the wall, and further along he could see another doing the same, and the Others kept coming, and they kept dying. The smell that came off the hissing, bubbling bodies stung his eyes and threatened to make him gag as it hit the back of his throat, but he kept pumping.

"Check the barrels!" he shouted at the Warden. "We can't let them run dry."

"Too late," the big man replied. There was a sucking sound as his pump brought up air. He dropped the bellows.

"To me!" the big man shouted. "More water! More garlic!"

At the same time Sean's bellows began to wheeze. He turned, and saw a convoy of children labouring with buckets and gourds, heading for the wall, but it would be long seconds before they would be able to replenish his weapon. One final squeeze left barely a dribble coming from the spout.

Sean dropped the bellows and unsheathed his sword as the black swarm began to slowly make their way up the wall over their twice dead.

The sound of the pipes wafted up to the high tower and in to Martin's bedchamber.

"What in Jesu's name is that?" Martin asked. "Are they skinning something alive?"

There was just a trace of a grim smile on Campbell's lips.

"Don't mock the pipes, laddie, they stir the blood in battle. If you have any to stir. It pains me greatly to hear them in these circumstances. They should be heard skirling for the dancing, or as a backdrop for the old stories, not in the employ of the dark ones," he said.

Martin could not imagine that sound ever being employed for anything else—it spoke of battle and bloodlust, of death and destruction, and it drew a sharp dagger of fear up his spine as the screaming outside started again with renewed vigour.

"My friends, my family, are dying," Martin said. "We cannot stay here and do nothing."

Campbell looked grim. His eyes never left the door as he spoke.

"But that is exactly what we must do, until our time comes. Your father has it right—do not be so quick to embrace the inevitable. It will come in its own time."

There was a movement in the adjoining chamber. The curtain parted, and Mary Campbell came through. Martin started when he realised that the Boy King's vision was a true one—she was dressed exactly as he had foreseen. The difference was that the spell seemed broken and her eyes were clear. She looked lost and confused.

"Father?" she said. "Where are we? What is happening here?"

Campbell turned towards her, sudden tears in his eyes. He pulled her close in an embrace, and that was when Barnstable appeared in the doorway behind him, an already bloodied sword raised.

Martin took it all in with one glance—the blank-eyed stare and the rigidity of the man's limbs told the story, and he knew that the Boy King had found another conduit for his will.

"Look out!" he managed to shout, but the sword was already descending and Campbell could only try to dodge it as he turned. He attempted to push his daughter away, out of danger, but she held on tight to him, and Martin could see the blank stare back in her eyes and the evil smile on her lips. The blade caught the side of the Scotsman's head and sent him sprawling, unmoving, to the ground.

Martin tried once again to rise from the bed, but his legs betrayed him by refusing to move. In frustration he threw his sword at the Constable, but it merely bounced harmlessly off the wall by his head.

Barnstable threw back his head and laughed, then a voice that Martin had previously only heard inside his head came from his lips.

"Don't worry. I have already promised that you can have her when I am finished with her."

The Constable took Mary Campbell in an embrace, a grotesque parody of the earlier one between father and daughter.

"She is a beauty, is she not?" the big man said, running his hand down her spine and caressing her buttocks. "I chose well."

He slapped the girl lightly across the face.

"Show some appreciation, woman. I will make your son a prince, surely that is worth something?"

And she groaned, but somehow Martin knew that it was not her own voice.

Whatever had hold of Barnstable suddenly seemed to get bored of the situation.

"Come, my dear. Let us get you to a place of safety where you can rest and grow strong—these day-dwellers have had you running all over the country, and that is not a fit pursuit for a royal bride."

He took her by the hand and led her from the room while Martin shook in rage and frustration, hot tears blinding his eyes.

The first Other came over the wall slowly, almost cautiously.

It had been Other for a long time. Its eyes were fiery red pits sunk beneath a heavy brow. Lank white hair hung in rattails and its fingernails were long and torn. It wore nothing apart from a short kilt, but blood had been daubed across its white bony chest in heavy strips, giving the appearance of clothing. It smiled, showing yellow, chipped fangs and climbed onto the top of the wall as Sean stepped forward to meet it.

His first cut took it in the neck, but was not firm enough to take the head off, and the Other was fast enough to grip him on the upper arm, long nails taking hold through the cloth of his shirt. The wound in its neck gaped, but there was no blood, only a wedge of grey, dead flesh.

Sean let his shoulder drop and threw the creature over his back and away from him, feeling something tear at his arm as the fingernails were torn from his skin. Pirouetting, he brought the sword round at head height, catching the Other full in the neck before it had even fully regained its balance and sending its head spinning to reach the ground just before the body.

Two more were on him before he even had time to draw his sword back. He thrust the first away from him, gaining a temporary respite, but the second was already reaching for him. He got his sword up, and fangs clashed against steel instead of flesh. With no room to manoeuvre, he head butted the Other, knocking it temporarily to its knees where he was able to thrust the point of his sword through its mouth and out the back of its neck. But when he tried to withdraw, he found the sword caught tight between the Other's jaws.

Before he could pull the sword free, the second Other returned and grabbed at his shoulders. He threw his weight backwards, dragging the pinioned Other along with him, and all three fell the ten feet off the wall to the courtyard below, the creature beneath him taking the weight of all three bodies. Sean felt the rib cage crush beneath him, and when he managed to roll off, white watery fluid was spouting from a wound in its chest where bones had pierced through to the heart.

The second creature still had teeth locked on his sword,

and its pale hands fluttered around the blade. Sean tugged at the sword but was still unable to dislodge it from the jaws. The creature laid its hands on the weapon and began pulling itself along it towards him. He let go and stepped inside the creature's fumbling grasp, kicking it twice in the head before grabbing it in a wrestling lock and twisting hard. He allowed himself a grim smile as he heard the vertebrae snap, and, with the creature thrashing on the ground, he was finally able, using its head as leverage, to retrieve his sword and send the Other to meet its maker.

Sean's breath came in short, sharp hitches and he had to force himself to be calm. He looked around him. The air was full of the screams of the dying and the long since dead. Up on the wall the Warden was still struggling with a large Other, a monster of a creature even bigger than he was, the pair of them locked in a clinch, the Warden with his head pushed down into the Other's chest to protect his neck. Even as Sean watched, the Other heaved and lifted, bringing the Warden's feet off the ground, threatening to toss him over the wall. Without thinking, Sean threw his sword like a spear. Although his aim was not true, the hilt caught the creature above the eye, and it screamed as a blue flame suddenly flickered there. The Warden fell, his buttocks striking the lip of the ledge before his body dropped down into the courtyard. He hit with a crunch, and Sean saw blood spurt as a bone smashed in his leg, the sheared end punching a hole through the skin.

The large Other, screaming still, dropped on the wounded man, fangs bared, enraged at the sight and smell of the blood. The Warden, his face as pale as an Other, managed to throw himself to one side, kicking out with his good leg as the pale beast grabbed for him. The Other staggered and swayed slightly but kept its balance and moved forward once more.

Sean didn't have time to think. He threw himself forward onto the Other's broad shoulders, aware as he did so that he was weaponless. The creature tried to reach for him, hands curled into claws, but Sean managed to wrap his legs around its waist and was working his own hands towards its eyes.

He got his thumbs into the soft flesh at the side of the

Other's eyes and began to gouge, bringing a hiss from it. The creature thrashed under him, then it suddenly fell away beneath him.

As he fell he saw the Warden under them drag his sword across the back of the creature's knees. They fell together as if toppled by a forester's axe.

Sean tried to throw himself to one side, but he was too entangled and he had no time. He took the brunt of the fall, the Other's weight driving all the breath from him. He unclasped his legs from the Other's waist and rolled to one side, pushing himself upright and waiting for an attack.

He was still trying to get his breath, but the creature never came. The Warden was sitting on its chest and had its head in his hands. He banged it down, hard, on the ground and Sean saw the back of the skull collapse, but still the mouth worked and the fangs clicked together.

"Die, you bastard, die!" The Warden screamed and banged the head down, again and again, until there was only pulp beneath his hands.

Sean put a hand on the big man's shoulder, then had to stand back as the Warden turned, ready to fight. It was a long second before the fire died in his eyes and Sean felt safe in approaching him.

"Come on," he said, grabbing the man under the arms. "We need to get that leg looked at."

"No time," the Warden said, pointing towards the wall. "I don't think I'll be bleeding to death."

The Others were pouring over the wall, with no one left standing to stop them. Sean was about to throw himself among them when he heard a voice behind him.

"Officers of the watch fall back!"

Training prevailed over logic and he stepped away from the wall, dragging the Warden with him.

More black shadows appeared above him just as he was deafened by the roar of muskets from behind, and a volley of shots almost cleaved the attackers in two. And where the shot hit them, their bodies exploded in patches of white silver which flared so bright they left their impressions like ghosts in front of his eyes.

The Others fell away, but more followed, and they too were hit with a full volley of shots.

"Front rank reload, rear rank forward," he heard a familiar voice shout, just as the roar of muskets nearly deafened him.

Sean turned to see a line of old men, all armed with muskets, easing slowly forward, kneeling to reload as they came; another line standing up behind them to unleash another thunderous volley. Powder smoke hung heavy in the air and his ears rang in rebellion.

Menzies was leading operations.

"Not bad for a bunch of drunken old sots, eh?" he said. "Although the silver shot does help."

The musketmen advanced past where Sean was standing. He was astonished to see that the men were from Menzies' age group, and some were even older. Most wore uniforms of the watch, but ones in which the colours had faded and the cloth had thinned. He saw that some of their hands shook, but from the steel in their eyes, he didn't think it was from fear.

"Come on, boy!" Menzies shouted. "Or do you want to wait for us to kill them all? Get that barrel filled—we only have a limited supply of the shot, and it won't last long!"

Sean noticed that the trail of children with the water supplies were standing back behind the musketmen, who were even now advancing to the top of the wall. He motioned them forward, leading them up the steps to the barrel. As he moved to follow after them, the Warden groaned and clutched his leg before holding out a hand to Sean.

"I owe you a favour," the big man said.

"I'll collect if we get through the night," Sean replied, taking the hand and gripping, tight, to show the truth in it.

Already the musketmen were beginning to run out of shot, men peeling away from their ranks as they came up empty. Sean moved quickly to the top of the wall and grabbed hold of the bellows, waiting for the barrel to be full enough.

The massed horde of Others were already creeping closer

again. Their ranks were still being thinned by the volleys, but the sheer press of numbers was pushing them forwards.

At last the water reached a reasonable level and Sean shot a spray over the head of the riflemen as the noise reached a new pitch.

So the shooting went on, and Sean kept pumping, and the Others perished in their scores, but there came a time when all the riflemen were out of shot, and the water had again slowed to a trickle. Once more it was down to hand-to-hand fighting as the first of the Others came over the wall.

Sean found his sword lying on the wall where it landed and the weight of it in his hand gave him some comfort as he watched the screaming horde flow towards him.

He said a quiet prayer and prepared to die valiantly as the dark Others poured over the walls and the old men began to fall, one by one, around him.

He was forced backwards, down the steps, defending all the time, only just managing to keep the Others at bay until only he and Menzies remained standing over the Warden.

"We fought the good fight," Menzies said. The old man was breathing hard, but Sean had seen him wield a blade better than many a man half his age.

"That we did, sir. They will sing songs about us long after we are gone."

"If any are left to sing them," the Warden said. "Help me up. I would die like a man."

It took both of them to get the Warden to his feet. The man went pale and had to bite his lip to stop himself crying out, but he managed to stand, shakily, beside the other two. They stood in a small ring, watching the Others circle around them.

"Why don't they attack?" the Warden said. "Are they playing with us?"

"No. They fear my blade," Sean said, but the old man shook his head.

"No," he said, pointing back into the main courtyard. "I fear that their master has been dealing with matters of greater import."

The large figure of Constable Barnstable led Mary Campbell through the courtyard, and the Others moved to surround them like an honour guard with a married couple.

Martin's rage consumed him and gave him a burst of adrenaline that saw him get his legs out of the bed, but he could not get them under his body enough to lift him upright. In frustration he pushed down, hard, on his wounded arm, bringing pain so intense that it sent him down into a deep black faint.

He drifts in blackness so deep it is like velvet, and he knows not whether he is falling or rising. Shapes pass him there in the dark: his father, brow creased with worry; Campbell, blood streaming from a head wound; Sean, mouth agape and screaming silently; himself, arms crossed over his breast, eyes dead and skin already beginning to take on the pallor of the dead. He gives in to despair and lets the dark take him, and now he knows he is falling, swirling down to a black well where dim shadows wait.

Then the silence is broken. An air, sung by a voice he should remember, pierces the dark and he rises towards it, rises ever faster, away from where the shadows from the well grasp in failure at his ankles.

And in the distance, a light pulsing in time to the air leads him onwards. And in the light, giant figures stand in a circle, at first seeming to dance to the tune, then becoming still as he approaches and sees the small figure of the Woodsman Lennan inside the stones. He blinks, just once, and he is standing in front of the small man.

The air is crisp and clear and he can feel the wind on his cheeks and in his hair. He can smell the sea, and something else, an animal odour that is coming from the bundle which Lennan is holding out to him.

"This is yours," Lennan says, although his lips do not move, and the voice seems to come from the stones themselves. The bundle is unwrapped, and Martin sees a large silver skin of a wolf, washed, cleaned, dried and fashioned into a cloak.

"May the strength of the grey brother live on in you. This is your manhood gift from your brothers in the forest. May it empty your soul."

Martin stretches out a hand and touches the fur, feeling the wiry hair beneath his fingers, and at the same time feels his body being shaken as if by a giant hand. The scene around him begins to fade, and he makes a grasp for the cloak. Lennan thrusts it towards him, but he is only able to grab at a few hairs before the shaking tears him out of the circle and back, whirling through the dark, to his bedchamber. The last thing he sees is Lennan's face, full of sadness.

He opened his eyes, shaking his head as if to clear a persistent dream. The pain in his arm had lessened, and when he looked down he saw that there, in the palm of his left hand, lay five hairs, thick and grey, like those of a wolf.

He swung his legs completely out of the bed and pushed himself upright, using both hands. There was surprisingly little pain as he walked across the room, unsteadily at first, then faster as he saw the pool of blood which was forming around Campbell's head.

Sean threw himself forward, intent on reaching Mary Campbell, but the wall of Others repelled him, time after time, and although he hacked and cut with his sword, sending many of them to the ground finally dead, more filled their place. And they did not fight back, merely kept pace with Barnstable and the girl as they headed for the wall.

A voice came from Barnstable's mouth.

"Ah, the young Romeo," it said. "I must thank you for taking good care of my bride. As a reward for your faithfulness, and as I am not blind to the rules of chivalry, your life will be spared, just this once. But should we meet again, you will not find me so forgiving. Beware that our paths do not cross again."

Sean pushed forward with renewed vigour, screaming as he tried to get through the unyielding wall of flesh, until

Menzies finally pulled him back.

"It's no use, son. There are too many."

Barnstable was already climbing the steps to the battlements as Sean pushed the old doctor away. Once more he threw his sword, and this time his aim was true, hitting Barnstable in the back and penetrating a good six inches. But no blood flowed, and that huge body did not so much as quiver.

The loathsome voice merely laughed, an almost girlish giggle.

"A fair attempt. But you cannot kill that which my mind holds in dominion."

The Constable, or the thing that had hold of him, took Mary Campbell in his arms and leapt to the top of the wall.

"Be well," he said to Sean. "You have spirit, and a bit of the dark in you. There will be a place at my side in the Royal Court if you would take it."

Sean shouted an obscenity and once more ran forward, but another laugh came from Barnstable.

"I assure you that my mother was long dead before I was old enough to try," he said.

Without another word he jumped from the wall, followed swiftly by his dark guard.

Sean leapt to the battlements, and would himself have jumped over had not old Menzies held him back.

"It is suicide," the doctor said. "There will be other days. He will not kill her until she has served her time—he needs what she is carrying."

He pulled at Sean again, taking him away from the edge of the wall.

"Live to fight again," he said. "All is not yet lost."

Sean watched the white figure that was Mary Campbell being carried through the dark field to the greater darkness beyond. There was a schism in that darkness, and a group of figures broke off, taking the white figure with them, eastwards along the wall.

"They will be taking her north. To Edinburgh, if I'm not mistaken," Menzies said, and Sean finally realised that there was more to Mary Campbell's story than he knew. But that would have to wait—the black horde beyond the wall was massing once more. He looked around the fort, checking the state of the defending force, but was dismayed to find that Menzies and himself were the only two men standing, the Warden having slumped to the ground with his back to the wall.

"It was all for nothing," he said. "I have lost and will die here not knowing what has become of her."

Menzies shook his head and pointed out over the field. "I don't think we are to die. At least not tonight anyway."

The black army moved southwards, away from the wall, the Boy King in the midst of a greater blackness leading them onto the road to Carlisle.

"Farewell!" a voice boomed from afar. "I go after bigger prizes!"

They stood and watched as the horde left the field, finally merging into the night. Even then they stood for long minutes, barely believing that they yet lived.

Campbell was alive. His breathing was quick and shallow, and his pulse raced, but the cut on his head was mainly a scalp wound and it had already stopped bleeding. Martin raised his head on a pillow and left him there as he hefted his sword and made for the stairs, the wolf's hair still clutched tightly in his left fist.

He felt light, as if he was floating, and the pain in his arm had dulled to little more than a dull ache. Lennan's song started up and rang in circles inside his head, and once more the world sparkled around him.

He was aware that there was silence outside, and hoped that he had time yet to stop Barnstable. He had no idea how long he had been out, nor whether Lennan had really aided him, but he had the wolf's hairs, and, no matter how temporary, he had his strength back as he headed down the stone steps.

After the second turn, he became aware of a heavy, laboured breathing from below, and his heart sank. But the song still sustained him through the turns until he came upon a small figure huddled on the stairs, sitting in a pool of blood that shone black in his newfound sight and poured in an alarmingly long thread down the stairs away from him. It was only when he bent down closer that he realised that it was his father.

The song stopped, as quickly as it had come, and Martin's legs threatened to give way beneath him.

The small figure stretched out a bloodstained arm, revealing a deep, too deep, wound in his right side, a side that was soaked black in blood.

"Barnstable," the old man whispered, bubbles of blood bursting at his mouth, and Martin remembered the man's sword, already bloodied before it hit Campbell.

"Don't speak, Father," he said, his voice breaking, sobs filling his chest. "I'll get Menzies."

Martin stood, unsure of his next move, but was grabbed and pulled back down close to the old man's face.

"No time," the Thane said. "Tell Campbell I tried to keep my oath." He coughed, and a stream of blood ran from his mouth and nose. "Tell him I do not yet relieve him of his part of the bargain."

"Please don't speak." Martin said. "Save your breath."

"No need," the Thane said, and coughed, bringing more blood to his mouth. When he spoke again his voice was little more than a wet whisper. "I am going to be with your mother, so do not grieve. The harder part falls to you. You must be Thane, and, in time, deal with Barnstable. Remember—the Thane must be just. Revenge must not cloud your actions."

The speech seemed to be too much for the old man. He clasped Martin's hand tighter.

"I wish I had more time to know you. Be a better Thane than I was."

"I'll try to be as good as you," Martin said.

There was a rattle in the old man's throat and his head fell to his chest. Martin let out a shriek. He pushed the wolf's hairs into the old man's hand, hoping to transfer some of what had sustained him, but there was no grip in the Thane's fingers, and there was no longer the sound of liquid breathing.

A stray draught caught the hairs and whirled them away into the darkness as Martin's strength left him and he fell in a swoon over the dead body of his father.

End

ABOUT THE AUTHOR

William Meikle is a Scottish writer, now living in Canada, with twenty novels published in the genre press and over 300 short story credits in thirteen countries. His works span a variety of genres, including Horror, Fantasy, Mystery, and Science Fiction.

Printed in Great Britain
by Amazon